RUSSIAN
FAIRY TALES

RUSSIAN
FAIRY TALES

FOREWORD BY
POST WHEELER

SENATE

Russian Fairy Tales

First published in 1912 as *Russian Wonder Tales*
by A & C Black, London

This edition published in 1995 by Senate, an imprint of
Studio Editions Ltd, Princess House, 50 Eastcastle Street,
London W1N 7AP, England

Cover design © Studio Editions Ltd 1995

ISBN 1 85958 181 1

Printed and bound in Guernsey by
The Guernsey Press Co. Ltd

FOREWORD

THE Russian *skazki* (*skazatz* = to tell) are the mass of folk-tales distributed widely throughout all the Russias. Handed down by constant repetition from generation to generation, a possession common to peasant's hut and Prince's palace from a time when history did not exist, they are to-day, from Archangel to the Black Sea and from Siberia to the Baltic, almost as much a part of the life of the people as the language itself. Their adventures are linked to a hundred phrases in common parlance; their heroes peer from every page of Slavonic literature; and the delver in historic débris finds each stratum sown thick with *skazka* shards to the very bed-rock of legend.

To the casual eye the *skazki*, aside from their unfamiliar nomenclature, do not seem to differ greatly from the tales of other peoples. The wild and wonderful machinery has all the artifices which belong to the mass of folk-lore owned in common by the Indo-European group of nations. Here, however, the superficial resemblance in great measure ceases. It is seen that the true " fairy " element does not predominate. Not only are the relations between man and the spiritual world different, but that spiritual world itself is less familiar. The field of the *skazki* is not so much fairy-land as a natural wonderland, approaching in its variety and gorgeousness of surprise the Empire of the " Thousand Nights and a Night."

Who originated these tales? In what forms did they first appear? And how can one account for the enormous number of their variants, and the hold they possess upon the millions of the Slavonic race who tell them to their children every day?

Russia was long in asking herself these questions. Until little more than a century ago she considered the *skazki* of small interest to the world of culture. The earlier Russian writers regarded them with mild curiosity and had no conception of their origin. The first printed collection was not made until near the end of the eighteenth century and the next was half gone before the "scientific" collector appeared. Active interest in them then began to be manifested and it was not long before serious study had convinced students of the literature that not only did this submerged fiction of the people go back to the very beginnings of the Slavonic race, but that its tales were direct descendents of the primitive nature-myths and that their variants retained, in the guise of wonder stories for the child, the persisting fragments of a great original *epos* which at one time pictured the heathen mythology of the old Slavonians: that the presumed purpose-less nursery invention, in fact, deduced its high origin from the ancient gods themselves.

These older meanings, for the teller, vanished many centuries ago. The only things the *skazki* picture that are common to Russian country life to-day are those things which in Russia never change—the wide, wind-swept *steppe* and dense forest, the love of animal life and the comradeship of the horse, the dread and terror of the long winter cold and the passionate welcome given to the springtime sun. What-ever else they may tell the student is in a tongue now unintelligible to the peasant, who has least of all been aware that, in these centuries-old repetitions there have been handed down to a new era pictures indelible, though blurred and indistinct, of an ancient age, of times, customs, religion and deities no longer his own.

For the beginning of the *skazki* we must go back to the remote time when the early Slavonians, parting from the parent stock in Central Asia, reached the Russias, developing there their myth-mass and setting up their hierarchy of Pagan gods. These gods, good and evil, were personifications of the forces of nature. The religion of which they were the *foci* was thus a nature-religion, and upon it was grafted a system of ancestor-worship not greatly different from other Oriental forms. And the race's conceptions of these gods and the material world, the soul, the birth and passing of human life, the individual's relations to the deities and his fellows, and the manifold observances in which beliefs and customs were enshrined, were embodied in a mass of myths, all more or less variations of the primal solar-myth with which all nations seem to have begun their cosmogonies.

The dawn of Christianity—late in Russia—marked the sunset of these ancient deities. The new Byzantine faith, in its irresistible progress, either crushed out wholly their memories or transferred their attributes to the keeping of Christian saints, leaving their myths to struggle for existence against an ever-increasing weight of foreign legend. And as the form of the old Pagan religion merged more and more into the new, these myths sank beneath the surface of the everyday life of the people, while the primitive mythology, with its symbolism, was forgotten.

The demiurge became first the merely supernatural being, man's henchman or servitor, and the ethereal abode of the old gods merely a mysterious upper country beyond the visible sky, inhabited by magical creatures pictured in a group of tales which are the Slavonic equivalents of the " Jack and the Beanstalk " story. In the next step these supernatural beings descended to the plane of the pseudo-historic and finally merged into the real, becoming the old-time champions of the new faith, as, for example, the companions of Vladimir, who introduced Christianity into Russia. Lastly these faded into the purely imaginary. By this process the Slavonic god of the thunder (*Perun*) sank by gradual degrees, through Christian Paladin, to the conventional "Tzarevich Ivan" of the *skazki*, and in the last step to the friendly beast—the glowing bird, the heroic horse, the aid-giving wolf and bear—whose constant reappearance give the tales such a surprising variety of incident. The deities of evil underwent a like process, becoming the *Kastchey*, the *Baba-Yaga*, and the many malevolent beings which the *skazka* hero overcomes.

In lapse of time, too, the form of the myth deteriorated as had the content. The tales lost their coherency, becoming separated into episodes which in turn disintegrated to collections of mere fragments. These became localized in different versions, each of which retained or discarded detail at its provincial pleasure, the result being an incredible reduplication of variants of the same fundamental tale. An opposite process went on at the same time : similar fragments coalesced and grouped themselves about a single axis of incident, infinitely increasing the multiplication. So that the *skazki*, as they appear to-day, are less a cluster of individual tales than an elaborate mosaic, with whose fragments of colour and incident the modern adaptor (such as Pushkin or Ershoff) produces variant and highly-tinted designs, on the kaleido-scopic principle.

Such, in brief, is the genealogy of the Russian *skazki*, from the poetic symbolism of a primitive religion to the despised Cinderellas of fiction, from a revered drama of the high gods to a group of peasant " Old Wives' Tales."

It is a matter of regret that the English-speaking world has had little opportunity of acquaintance with these naïve, old-world stories, although they by no means suffer in comparison with the German *Märchen*, upon which there exists such a formidable literature in English. Mr. W. R. S. Ralston's " Russian Folk-Tales," published in 1873, was primarily less of a collection than a treatise on Slavonic folklore, and perhaps for this reason its engrossing and scholarly qualities failed to gain for the *skazki* a popularity they richly deserve. And beside this, so far as I am aware, but one other well-known collection is available. In 1874 Petr Nicolaevich Polevoi, the historian, published thirty-six of Afanasief's tales (with a single exception none of these was cited in Mr. Ralston's work) variously recombined and elaborated, in a volume intended for children, and of these versions twenty-five have been Englished by Mr. R. Nisbet Bain.

The twelve tales of which the present volume consists are, in part, the result of an attempt to select types of those *motifs* of widest distribution throughout all the Russias, taking into account the number of distinct variants and the mass of population to which each is known. The attempt has been made, also, to combine cognate variants and to reconcile detail—the result in each case being in a sense a composite—and to treat each in somewhat of the method and manner of the folk-tales of Western Europe.

A word, however brief, as to the modern *skazki* would be incomplete without a reference to Mr. Bilibin, whose wholly

charming illustrations, used herein with his permission, have
of recent years given them their peculiar artistic *cachet*. No
decorative artist in Russia has so allied himself with the
movement which has brought again into familiar use the
striking and characteristic conventions of Russian art of the
Middle Ages ; and it may be said that in no way has he more
endeared himself to the Russian people than by the exquisite
simplicity of method and fine appreciation of artistic values
which he has brought to his treatment of the *skazki*. In
these pictures he has made the old myths glow again in the
modern wonder tales which are so fresh and fair a part of the
youth of the Russian child, bequeathed to him from that
magical past and that enchanted land the memories of whose
marvels moved Pushkin's pencil when he wrote :

> " There is the Russian soul ! The very odour of Russia !
> There have I also been, and its honied drink have quaffed !
> I saw the green oak-tree beside the blue sea-ocean ;
> Beneath it I sat me down, to list while the learned cat
> Told me its stories !"

POST WHEELER.

St. Petersburg,
  August 20, 1911.

"CABINET DU MINISTRE DE L'INSTRUCTION PUBLIQUE,
ST. PETERSBURG,
June 14/27, 1911.

"DEAR MR. WHEELER,

"Accept a word of congratulation upon your charming collection of 'Russian Wonder Tales,' which I have read—with your Foreword on the *skazki*—with much interest and attention. Your English rendition of these old, poetic stories is in all points accurate and in complete accordance with the original texts. Yours is a most attractive treatment, and I regard the book as a very valuable contribution to our Russian folk-lore.

"With my best regards, believe me,
"Sincerely yours,
"L. CASSO,
"*Imperial Russian Minister of Education.*"

"POST WHEELER, ESQUIRE,
Chargé d'Affaires,
American Embassy,
St. Petersburg."

CONTENTS

TZAR SALTAN

RUSSIAN WONDER TALES

TZAR SALTAN

In ancient days, long before our time, in a certain Tzardom of a realm far beyond the blue sea-ocean, there was a Tzar, young in years, named Saltan, who was so handsome and so clever that songs were sung and tales told of him, and beautiful maidens everywhere dreamt of him at night. Minded to rule his Tzardom well, he used to wander forth at dusk in all four directions of his capital, in order to see and hear, and thus he perceived much good and much evil and saw many strange sights. One evening, as he passed the house of a rich merchant, he saw through the window three lovely damsels, the merchant's daughters, sitting at their needlework, and drawing near he overheard their conversation.

The eldest said: " If the Tzar were to wed me,

I would grind flour so fine that the like of the
bread I would bake from it could not be found
in the whole world."

The Tzar, hearing, thought: "That would be
good bread truly; however, the bread I eat now
is not so bad."

The second said: "If the Tzar were to wed me,
I would weave for him a *kaftan*[1] of gold and silver
thread, so that he would shine like the Glowing
Bird."

"That would be good weaving, indeed," thought
the Tzar; "though little enough need have I for
such a splendid coat."

Then the youngest daughter, who was named
Marfa, said: "As for me, if the Little Father
Tzar became my husband, I know how neither
to spin nor to weave, but I would bear him seven
hero-sons like bright falcons, that should be the
comeliest in his Tzardom; and their legs should
be golden to the knee and their arms silver to
the elbow, and in their hair should be little stars."

Tzar Saltan, listening, was well pleased with this
speech. "Glad would I be to be the father of
seven such sons," he said to himself; and returning

[1] Great-coat.

to his Palace, he summoned his Boyars[1] and Court Ministers, and despatched them to the house of the merchant to bring his youngest daughter, whom he purposed to make his Tzaritza. He ordered a great festival and spread tables of oak, at which all the folk of the Tzardom ate, drank and made merry.

On the third day he and the merchant's daughter were married, and slept on an ivory bed, and began to live together, soul with soul, in all joy and contentment. The two elder daughters of the merchant, however, were envious; one sulked over her oven and the other wept over her loom, and both hated their sister because the Tzar had preferred her over them.

Now there was war in those days and whether after a long time or a short time, it became necessary for Tzar Saltan to take the field. Tzaritza Marfa wept long and would not be comforted; so before he departed he sent for her two sisters to remain with her until his return. And they, although they hated their sister, pretending great love for her, came at once to the Palace. So the Tzar mounted his good horse and

[1] Noblemen.

bidding his wife care for herself for his sake, rode away to the fight.

It befell when the Tzar had been three months absent that three babes were born to his Tzaritza—such lovely little sons that their like cannot be told or described, but can only be imagined, and each had legs golden to the knee, arms silver to the elbow, and little stars in his hair set close together. And Tzaritza Marfa sent to her husband a fleet messenger to tell him of their birth.

Her sisters, however, kept back the messenger and sent another in his place with this message: "Thy Tzaritza, our sister, who boasted that she would bear thee Princes of gold and silver, hath borne thee now neither sons nor daughters, but instead, three wretched little kittens."

Then they bribed the nurses and attending women, took from the Tzaritza, while she slept, the three boy-babies, and put in their jewelled cradles three kittens. As for the beautiful children, they gave them to a Baba-Yaga,[1] and the cruel old witch put them into an underground room, in a forest, under a crooked oak-tree, whose entrance was closed by a great flat stone.

[1] Witch Grandmother.

When the Tzar heard the words of the messenger, he was greatly angered. He sent orders to throw the kittens into the sea-ocean, and was minded also to kill his wife. This, however, he could not bear to do, so much did he love her. "I will forgive this fault," he said to himself. "Perchance she may yet give me sons fit for a Tzar."

He returned at length to his Tzardom, and lived with his wife happily as before, till there was held a great hunt on the open *steppe*,[1] and he rode away to kill wild geese and swans. And scarce had he been gone three days, when two more sons were born to his wife, the Tzaritza Marfa—such lovely babes that one could not look sufficiently at them, —and each had legs golden to the knee, arms silver to the elbow, and little stars in his hair clustering close together.

The Tzaritza sent in haste for a nurse, and the servant, as it happened, met on his way the old witch. "Where dost thou haste so fast?" she asked him.

"Not far," he replied.

"Tell me instantly," said the Baba-Yaga, grinding her teeth, "or it will be the worse for thee!"

---

[1] Plain.

" Well," said the servant, " if thou must know, I go to fetch a nurse to the Palace, for two hero-sons have just been born to our mistress, the Tzaritza."

" Take me as nurse," commanded the witch.

" That I dare not," the servant replied, " lest the Tzar, on his return, strike my head from off my shoulders."

" Obey me," snarled the Baba-Yaga, " or meet a worse fate this instant !"

The servant, trembling for his life, returned with the old witch, who, as soon as she came in to the Tzaritza Marfa, took from her, while she slept, the two lovely babes, put in their place under the sable coverlet two blind puppies, and carried the children to the underground room in the forest. Having done this, she told the two sisters, who, hastening to the Palace, bribed the serving-women and despatched a messenger to the Tzar to say : " Our sister, thy Tzaritza, who boasted that she would bear thee Tzareviches of silver and gold, hath borne thee now neither sons nor daughters, but instead two miserable little puppies."

When the messenger brought him this message, the Tzar's anger waxed hot. He ordered the puppies to be thrown into the sea-ocean, and would have slain his wife but for his great love. However, after his anger had softened, he said to himself: " This second fault also I will pass over. Perchance even yet she will bear me sons fit for a Tzar." And, returning to his capital, he lived happily with her as before.

It happened at length that the Tzar went to a distant Tzardom to pay a visit of ceremony, and this time he set a strong guard about the Palace, with strict command to allow no one whatever to go in or out. When he had been absent six months, two more babes were born to the Tzaritza—sons of a loveliness that is known only in a tale, with legs golden to the knee, arms silver to the elbow, and with little stars in their hair. And the Tzaritza, deeming herself safe by reason of the guard about the Palace, bade them peal all the bells for joy.

Hearing the rejoicing, the sisters guessed what had occurred, and sent at once for the Baba-Yaga, who by a witch's charm caused a deep sleep to fall upon all the guardsmen so that each slumbered where he stood, and she herself entered the Palace. When the Tzaritza saw her, however, she hid one of the babes, whom she had named Guidon, in her sleeve, so that the Baba-Yaga, though she carried

away the other, did not see it.   In place of the babe,
the old witch left a piece of wood, and the sisters, as
before, bribed the attendants, and sent a messenger
to the Tzar to say : " Thy Tzaritza, our sister, who
boasted that she would bear thee sons of gold and
silver, hath borne thee now neither son nor daughter,
neither is it a frog nor a snake, but a little log of
wood."

When the Tzar heard this message, he well-nigh
lost his senses in the violence of his rage.   After his
anger had somewhat subsided, he ordered the log of
wood to be thrown into the sea-ocean, and sent a
letter to his Prime Minister, bidding him call
together his Boyars and Princes of all the Realm to
consider the matter on his return.

The messenger rode back with the royal letter,
but the two wicked sisters met him on his way, and
by stealth stole the letter from his pocket and put
in its place another, which read : " I, Tzar Saltan,
bid my Boyars without delay to seize the Tzaritza,
put her into a chest bound with iron, and cast it
into the deepest abyss of the sea-ocean."

The messenger delivered the letter, and at once
the Boyars came to the Tzaritza and told her the
cruel decree.   They pitied her and wept with her.

but there was nothing to be done, since the Tzar's will was law, and the same day, with the babe still hidden in her sleeve, she was put into a chest bound with iron, and it was thrown into the wide sea-ocean.

Soon after the Tzar returned, ready, so great was his love, to forgive his wife a third time. But it was then too late, and, thinking that the Tzaritza was drowned, he at length married the elder of the two sisters, and brought them both to live in his Palace.

Whether the chest floated a long time or a short time in the sea-ocean, on smooth water or rough water, the little Guidon, who had been hidden in the Tzaritza's sleeve, was growing like wheat-flour when new yeast is added to it, not by days but by hours, until at length he began to speak.

"Little mother," he said, "I have not room enough. Let me stretch myself!"

"Nay, little soul," she answered. "I hear no sound of the waves lapping on the sand. The water is deep beneath us. If thou dost stretch we shall be drowned."

The chest floated on and on, and at length its bottom began to scratch against hard pebbles.

Then the little boy said : "We touch something, little mother. May I stretch myself?"

She gave him permission, and he began to stretch himself, and so strong and sturdy was he that the iron bands broke asunder and the chest fell to pieces. Looking about them, they saw that they were on an island, which had a high hill, sloping down to a green field, surrounded by a forest. The mother and her son crossed the field and entered the forest, searching for a path that should lead them to some habitation. They found none, however, and were about to return wearied to the meadow, when Tzarevich Guidon came upon a purse lying on the ground.

Opening it, they found a flint and steel, and were glad, thinking that with a fire they could protect themselves against cold and wild beasts. Tzarevich Guidon struck the flint and steel together, when instantly there appeared a sharp axe and a huge hammer.

"Here we are, Master," said the axe and hammer. "By God's blessing, by the Order of the Pike, what command wilt thou be pleased to lay upon us?"

"Build us a Palace to live in," answered Guidon, "and fetch us food and drink."

At once the axe flew at the trees and began to chop, square, and sharpen them, and the hammer to pound them into the earth for a foundation ; and while the Tzaritza and the Tzarevich watched, there began to rise on the edge of the forest a Palace of white stone, with battlemented walls, more splendid than has ever been seen in any Tzardom, richer than can be guessed or imagined, whose like can neither be told in a tale or written with a pen. They entered it, and found therein whatever the soul could ask.

Now, before many days it befell that a ship came sailing that way, and the shipmen wondered greatly to see there, on what had been an uninhabited island, a stately Palace, with golden domes and walls of white stone, and they landed to see this marvel.

The Tzaritza met them and made them her guests, giving them food and drink to their hearts' desire.

" O merchants," she said, " in what trade are ye concerned, and whither sail ye from here ?"

They answered : " We have traded in the skins of sables and black foxes in foreign marts ; now we sail to the east, to the Tzardom of Tzar Saltan the Glorious."

"A happy voyage to you," said the Tzaritza, "and give a greeting from me to Tzar Saltan."

The merchants re-embarked and sailed to the Tzardom of Tzar Saltan, who called them to be his guests; and they came before him, where he sat sad-faced on his golden throne, with his new wife and her sister by his side. As they sat at table the Tzar said: "O merchants and tradesmen! Have ye voyaged far, and to what lands went ye? Is it well or ill across the blue sea-ocean? And what new wonder is there in the white world?"

The shipmen replied: "O Tzar's Majesty! We travelled over all the world, and were on our way hither when we saw a new wonder more marvellous than any. There has been of old time in the sea-ocean an island, without inhabitants, save they were wizards or wild beasts. It had a great flat meadow on which grew a single oak-tree, and about it was a dense forest. So hath it always been; yet but now, as we came to it, we found there a splendid Palace, with towers whose tops were golden, and with green gardens about it. In it dwells a beautiful Tzaritza and a Tzarevich, and the Tzarevich has legs golden to the knee, and arms silver to the elbow, and in his hair are little stars. We landed there, and the Tzaritza entertained us royally, and sent a greeting to thee."

Tzar Saltan wondered greatly to hear, and said: "As God lets me live, I will visit this wonderful island and see it with my own eyes." But his wicked wife and her younger sister, not wishing him to go, began to sneer.

"A Palace on an island! What is that to be compared to a marvel of which I can tell thee?"

"What marvel is that?" asked the Tzar.

She answered: "Across three times nine countries, in the thirtieth Tzardom, there is a green garden, and in the garden is a mill which grinds of itself. It winnows the grain and throws the chaff a hundred *versts* [1] away. By the mill stands a golden column, and up and down the column climbs a learned cat. As it goes up it sings songs, and as it comes down it tells stories."

Hearing of this new wonder, the Tzar gave up his purpose to visit the island.

The merchants, having loaded their ship with other goods, sailed on a second voyage, and, passing the Tzaritza's island, cast anchor, and were again entertained; and they recounted there how Tzar

---

[1] One *verst* = 3,500 feet, English.

Saltan had desired to sail thither till his wife had told him of the mill, the golden column, and the story-telling cat.

As soon as they had made their farewells and sailed away, Tzarevich Guidon took from the purse the flint and steel, and struck them sharply together, and immediately the axe and the hammer appeared, saying: "Here we are, thy servants! By God's blessing, by the Order of the Pike, what dost thou bid us do?"

"I will have, near this Palace," said the Tzarevich, "a mill which grinds and winnows of itself and throws the chaff a hundred *versts* away. By it must be a column of gold on which climbs a cat, telling tales and singing songs."

At once the axe and hammer disappeared, and, next morning, when he went to his balcony, the Tzarevich saw that the garden, the mill. the golden column, and the clever cat had all been brought as he had commanded.

He caused his servants, the axe and hammer, to build by the column a crystal summer-house, in which the cat should live, and each day the Tzaritza and Tzarevich Guidon amused themselves by listening to its songs and stories.

HE SAW, THROUGH THE WINDOW, THREE LOVELY DAMSELS

Time passed, and again the ship returned from her voyage, and the merchants wondered to see the new marvels. They landed, and the Tzaritza, meeting them, bade them enter and taste of her hospitality. She gave them honey to eat and milk to drink, and treated them so handsomely that they scarce knew themselves for pleasure. "O tradesmen," she asked them, "what do ye barter, and whither sail ye from here?"

"We have bartered carpets and stallions from the Don around the whole world," they answered. "Now we sail to the eastward, to the Tzardom of Tzar Saltan the Mighty."

"A good journey to you," said the Tzaritza. "Bear to Tzar Saltan greeting from my son, Tzarevich Guidon."

The merchants spread sail and voyaged to the Tzardom of Tzar Saltan, and a second time he summoned them to bear him company. And as they ate and drank in his sumptuous hall, he asked them: "O tradesmen and mariners, doubtless ye have traversed the whole earth. What have ye seen, and what news do ye bear? And is there any new marvel in the white world?"

They answered: "O mighty Tzar Saltan! we

have truly visited many countries and seen many
strange things, but the most wonderful is this.
When we were thy guests before, we told thee of an
island on which, bare and uninhabited of old, we
found a splendid Palace with a beautiful Tzaritza
and a brave Tzarevich. On this sailing we passed
again that way and put in at the island, and now
beside the Palace of white stone there is a green
garden with a mill that grinds and winnows of
itself and casts the chaff a hundred *versts* away.
Beside it is a golden column on which a cat climbs
continually up and down, singing songs and telling
tales.   And there is a summer-house of crystal in
which the cat lives.   The Tzaritza showed us these
wonders and her son the Tzarevich Guidon sends a
greeting to thee."

When Tzar Saltan heard this, again was he
seized with a desire to see the island, but, as before,
his evil wife and her sister sneered and the wife
said :

"A rare thing in truth !   Thinkest thou the mill
and cat are so wonderful ?   What, indeed, are they
beside a marvel of which I know ?"

"What is that ?" asked the Tzar.

She answered : " Across three times nine lands,

in the thirtieth Tzardom, there is a wood and in the wood a fir-tree. On the tree lives a squirrel, cracking nuts with his teeth. These are not ordinary nuts, for their shells are of gold and the kernels of emerald. He who owns this wonder is the richest Tzar in all the world, for his wealth never ceases to increase until it cannot be reckoned."

And, deeming this an even greater marvel, Tzar Saltan again laid by his purpose to visit the island.

The merchants filled their ship with new merchandise and set sail for distant lands and, passing the island again, were welcomed by Tzaritza Marfa and Tzarevich Guidon, to whom they recounted their visit to Tzar Saltan. Nor did they fail to tell how he had purposed to sail thither until he had heard of the fir-tree, the squirrel and the nuts of gold and emerald.

When they had departed, Tzarevich Guidon struck together his flint and steel, and the axe and hammer, appearing, said: "Master, we are here! By God's blessing, by the Order of the Pike, what wilt thou that we accomplish?"

"Plant me here," said the Tzarevich, "a fir-tree. On it let there be a squirrel which cracks with its teeth nuts whose shells are of gold and their kernels of emerald."

The axe and hammer disappeared and next day, when he arose, the Tsarevich found all done as he had commanded. He bade them build a summer-house of crystal for the squirrel to live in, and the golden shells and emeralds he put into the Palace treasury till the wealth could not be reckoned.

It befell at length that the merchants' ship returned from its voyage and cast anchor at the island. The Tzaritza met and welcomed them, giving them to eat and drink till for rich feasting they scarce remembered their names. "O shipmen and merchants," she said, "what merchandise do ye bear and whither fare ye from here?"

They answered: "We are laden with steel swords and with precious armour which we have traded through the whole world, and our way is eastward, to the Tzardom of Tzar Saltan the Magnificent."

"A fair wind to you," said the Tzaritza. "Carry my greeting, and that of my son Guidon, to Tzar Saltan."

So they sailed on to the Tzar's dominions and a third time were summoned to his presence and

feasted; and before they left him he said : " O
merchants and travellers, in all your wayfaring
what new sights have ye seen ? And is there any
fresh marvel in the white world ?"

" O Tzar's majesty !" they replied. " We told
thee before of the island with its Palace, its self-
grinding mill, its golden column and its learned
cat. On this voyage also we visited it and were
entertained right royally. And now, in addition to
the other wonders we recounted, there is there a fir-
tree, on which sits a squirrel, cracking with its teeth
nuts, whose shells are gold and whose kernels are
emerald. The squirrel lives in a crystal summer-
house and the gold and emeralds are piled in the
Palace treasury till it overflows with such riches
that the like is surely not to be seen in the whole
world. The noble Tzarevich Guidon showed us
these things, and we bear to thee a greeting from
him and from the Tzaritza, his mother."

The Tzar was astonished to hear of this and said
to his wife : " In truth, the wonders of which thou
hast told me are all to be found in this surpassing
island. Canst thou recall any marvel to match
this ?"

She answered spitefully : " That is not so hard.

There is in a dense forest, under a crooked oak-tree, a great flat stone which covers an underground room, and in the room are six Tzareviches, more beautiful than can be told. Each has legs golden to the knee, arms silver to the elbow, and in his hair are little stars. A witch keeps them hidden, and there lives in the white world no man clever enough to find them out or to learn who they are."

Tzar Saltan, hearing, was silent, thinking of his dead wife and of her promise to bear him such hero-sons. He dismissed the merchants with rich gifts and they bought goods to fill their ships and sailed away again on the wide sea-ocean.

In time they touched at the island of Tzaritza Marfa, and being entertained, recounted to her their visit to Tzar Saltan's Court and told how, for a third time, he had purposed to voyage thither, until his wife had told of the underground room, and of the six Tzareviches with legs golden, arms of silver, and with stars in their hair.

When the shipmen had departed on their way, Tzaritza Marfa told Tzarevitch Guidon the story of her life with Tzar Saltan and what she had suffered at the hands of her wicked sisters. "These six Tzareviches," she said, "whom the witch hides in the forest, are surely none other than my own dear sons and thy little brothers. Let us depart to search for them."

So the Tzarevich struck together his flint and steel and bade the axe and hammer build a ship which would fly either on land or sea and which should take them to the witch's forest. Next morning all was ready, and they straightway embarked and sailed over the sea-ocean, and over the open *steppe* to the edge of the forest, where the Baba-Yaga had hidden the stolen Princes.

Whether the journey was long or short, whether it took a twelvemonth or a day, they found the crooked oak-tree and the Tzarevich lifted the great flat stone and they entered the underground room. They looked here and there and presently saw six little soiled shirts lying on chairs. The Tzaritza took them, washed them clean, rinsed, wrung and hung them to dry. Six little plates sat on a table unwashed. She washed them all and dried them and swept the floor. Hearing a noise outside, she said : "Someone is coming. Let us hide behind the stove."

They hid themselves, and the six Tzareviches entered, all with legs golden to the knee, arms silver

to the elbow, and with little stars in their hair.
They saw how the room had been swept and the
plates and shirts made clean, and were glad.
" Show thyself," they cried, "thou who hast washed
and tidied our house. If thou art a beautiful girl,
thou shalt be our little sister, and if thou art a
Tzaritza, thou shalt be our little mother !"

Then Tzaritza Marfa showed herself, and the six
Tzareviches ran to her, and she took them in her
arms and kissed and caressed them and told them
who they were—that she was indeed their mother
and Tzarevich Guidon their little brother. She
brought them from the forest to the magic ship,
and it sailed with them like a white swan, over the
open *steppe* and the blue sea-ocean to the Tzaritsa's
island, to her Palace of white stone, and there they
began to live happily together.

Now when its voyage was finished, the ship of
the merchants came back from the ends of the
world and put in at the island. The Tzaritza
welcomed them and she and her seven sons gave
them such feasts and amusements that for delight
they would have remained there for ever. " O
merchant-travellers," she asked them, " in what
cargoes do ye traffic, and whither go ye from here ?"

"We have sailed about the whole world," they answered, "with goods of every sort that tradesmen carry, and from here our course lies eastward to the Tzardom of Tzar Saltan the Splendid."

"Fair weather to you," she said, "and take a greeting to Tzar Saltan from me and from these my seven sons."

The ship departed, and when it was come to the Tzardom of Tzar Saltan, he made the merchants yet again his guests. And as they ate and drank and made merry, he said to them: "O tradesmen and far-journeying adventurers, ye have sailed to the uttermost lands. What strange thing have ye seen, and is there any new wonder in the white world?"

"O great Tzar Saltan!" they replied, "thou didst hear from us before of the island in the blue sea-ocean, of its Tzaritza and her Tzarevich, and their Palace of white stone, with the marvels there to be seen. On our way hither we again stopped there, and now the lady hath with her not one Tzarevich but seven, so handsome that we know no words to tell thee of them, and each has legs golden to the knee, and arms silver to the elbow, and in their hair are little stars set close together.

And when we departed the Tzaritza sent to thee greeting from herself and these seven sons."

When the merchants spoke thus the wicked wife of Tzar Saltan opened her mouth to speak, but the Tzar rose up and silenced her.

"Tell me no more of thy marvels," he said to her. "What am I, a Tzar or a child?" And having dismissed the merchants with presents, he sent for his Ministers and Boyars and bade a fleet to be prepared, and that same day set sail for the island.

Tzarevich Guidon, sitting with his brothers at the window, saw the ships of Tzar Saltan coming over the blue sea-ocean, and called to his mother, "See, our little father is coming!" He went to meet him and brought him into the Palace to the Tzaritza.

Seeing her, Tzar Saltan recognized her, and his breath stopped and his face flowed with tears. He kissed her and embraced his seven sons and all began to weep and rejoice together.

When they had spent some days in such happiness, they went aboard the ships and sailed back to Tzar Saltan's realm. He summoned his Ministers and Boyars, his Princes and Judges, and they condemned his evil wife, and she and her sister were put into a chest barred and bound with iron, and the chest was thrown into the sea-ocean. But God did not protect them as He had protected the Tzaritza and her son, for they sank at once into the lowest abyss and were drowned.

But Tzar Saltan and Tzaritza Marfa, with the seven Tzareviches, lived always together in bright-faced joy, and increased in all good things. And Tzaritza Marfa was as beautiful in her old age as she had been in her youth.

WASSILISSA THE BEAUTIFUL

WASSILISSA THE BEAUTIFUL

In a certain Tzardom, across three times nine kingdoms, beyond high mountain - chains, there once lived a merchant. He had been married for twelve years, but in that time there had been born to him only one child, a daughter, who from her cradle was called Wassilissa the Beautiful. When the little girl was eight years old the mother fell ill, and before many days it was plain to be seen that she must die. So she called her little daughter to her, and taking a tiny wooden doll from under the blanket of the bed, put it into her hands and said:

" My little Wassilissa, my dear daughter, listen to what I say, remember well my last words and fail not to carry out my wishes. I am dying. and with my blessing, I leave to thee this little doll. It is very precious for there is no other like it in the whole world. Carry it always about with thee in thy pocket and never show it to anyone. When

evil threatens thee or sorrow befalls thee, go into
a corner, take it from thy pocket and give it something to eat and drink. It will eat and drink
a little, and then thou mayest tell it thy trouble
and ask its advice, and it will tell thee how to act
in thy time of need." So saying, she kissed her
little daughter on the forehead, blessed her, and
shortly after died.

Little Wassilissa grieved greatly for her mother,
and her sorrow was so deep that when the dark
night came, she lay in her bed and wept and did
not sleep. At length she bethought herself of the
tiny doll, so she rose and took it from the pocket of
her gown and finding a piece of wheat-bread and a
cup of *kwas*,[1] she set them before it, and said:
"There, my little doll, take it. Eat a little, and
drink a little, and listen to my grief. My dear
mother is dead and I am lonely for her."

Then the doll's eyes began to shine like fire-flies,
and suddenly it became alive. It ate a morsel of the
bread and took a sip of the *kwas*, and when it had
eaten and drank, it said: "Don't weep, little
Wassilissa. Grief is worst at night. Lie down, shut
thine eyes, comfort thyself and go to sleep. The

---

[1] Beer.

morning is wiser than the evening." So Wassilissa
the Beautiful lay down, comforted herself and went
to sleep, and the next day her grieving was not so
deep and her tears were less bitter.

Now after the death of his wife, the merchant
sorrowed for many days as was right, but at the
end of that time he began to desire to marry again
and to look about him for a suitable wife. This was
not difficult to find, for he had a fine house, with a
stable of swift horses, besides being a good man
who gave much to the poor. Of all the women he
saw, however, the one who, to his mind, suited him
best of all, was a widow of about his own age with
two daughters of her own, and she, he thought,
besides being a good housekeeper, would be a kind
foster-mother to his little Wassilissa.

So the merchant married the widow and brought
her home as his wife, but the little girl soon found
that her foster-mother was very far from being
what her father had thought. She was a cold,
cruel woman, who had desired the merchant for
the sake of his wealth, and had no love for his
daughter. Wassilissa was the greatest beauty in
the whole village, while her own daughters were as
spare and homely as two crows, and because of this

all three envied and hated her. They gave her all
sorts of errands to run and difficult tasks to perform,
in order that the toil might make her thin and worn
and that her face might grow brown from sun and
wind, and they treated her so cruelly as to leave
few joys in life for her. But all this the little
Wassilissa endured without complaint, and while
the stepmother's two daughters grew always
thinner and uglier, in spite of the fact that they had
no hard tasks to do, never went out in cold or rain,
and sat always with their arms folded like ladies of
a Court, she herself had cheeks like blood and milk
and grew every day more and more beautiful.

Now the reason for this was the tiny doll, without whose help little Wassilissa could never have
managed to do all the work that was laid upon her.
Each night, when everyone else was sound asleep,
she would get up from her bed, take the doll into
a closet, and locking the door, give it something to
eat and drink, and say : " There, my little doll, take
it. Eat a little, drink a little, and listen to my grief.
I live in my father's house, but my spiteful stepmother wishes to drive me out of the white world.
Tell me ! How shall I act, and what shall I do ?"

Then the little doll's eyes would begin to shine

like glow-worms, and it would become alive. It
would eat a little food, and sip a little drink, and
then it would comfort her and tell her how to act.
While Wassilissa slept, it would get ready all her
work for the next day, so that she had only to rest
in the shade and gather flowers, for the doll would
have the kitchen garden weeded, and the beds of
cabbage watered, and plenty of fresh water brought
from the well, and the stoves heated exactly right.
And, besides this, the little doll told her how to
make, from a certain herb, an ointment which
prevented her from ever being sun-burnt. So all
the joy in life that came to Wassilissa came to her
through the tiny doll that she always carried
in her pocket.

Years passed, till Wassilissa grew up and became
of an age when it is good to marry. All the young
men in the village, high and low, rich and poor,
asked for her hand, while not one of them stopped
even to look at the stepmother's two daughters, so
ill-favoured were they. This angered their mother
still more against Wassilissa; she answered every
gallant who came with the same words: "Never
shall the younger be wed before the older ones!"
and each time, when she had let a suitor out of the

door, she would soothe her anger and hatred by beating her stepdaughter. So while Wassilissa grew each day more lovely and graceful, she was often miserable, and but for the little doll in her pocket, would have longed to leave the white world.

Now there came a time when it became necessary for the merchant to leave his home and to travel to a distant Tzardom. He bade farewell to his wife and her two daughters, kissed Wassilissa and gave her his blessing and departed, bidding them say a prayer each day for his safe return. Scarce was he out of sight of the village however, when his wife sold his house, packed all his goods and moved with them to another dwelling far from the town, in a gloomy neighbourhood on the edge of a wild forest. Here every day, while her two daughters were working indoors, the merchant's wife would send Wassilissa on one errand or other into the forest, either to find a branch of a certain rare bush or to bring her flowers or berries.

Now deep in this forest, as the stepmother well knew, there was a green lawn and on the lawn stood a miserable little hut on hens' legs, where lived a certain Baba-Yaga, an old witch grandmother. She lived alone and none dared go near the hut, for she ate people as one eats chickens. The merchant's wife sent Wassilissa into the forest each day, hoping she might meet the old witch and be devoured; but always the girl came home safe and sound, because the little doll showed her where the bush, the flowers and the berries grew, and did not let her go near the hut that stood on hens' legs. And each time the stepmother hated her more and more because she came to no harm.

One autumn evening the merchant's wife called the three girls to her and gave them each a task. One of her daughters she bade make a piece of lace, the other to knit a pair of hose, and to Wassilissa she gave a basket of flax to be spun. She bade each finish a certain amount. Then she put out all the fires in the house, leaving only a single candle lighted in the room where the three girls worked, and she herself went to sleep.

They worked an hour, they worked two hours, they worked three hours, when one of the elder daughters took up the tongs to straighten the wick of the candle. She pretended to do this awkwardly (as her mother had bidden her) and put the candle out, as if by accident.

"What are we to do now?" asked her sister.
"The fires are all out, there is no other light in all
the house, and our tasks are not done."

"We must go and fetch fire," said the first.
"The only house near is a hut in the forest, where
a Baba-Yaga lives. One of us must go and borrow
fire from her."

"I have enough light from my steel pins," said the
one who was making the lace, "and I will not
go."

"And I have plenty of light from my silver
needles," said the other, who was knitting the hose,
"and *I* will not go."

"Thou, Wassilissa," they both said, "shalt go
and fetch the fire, for thou hast neither steel pins
nor silver needles and cannot see to spin thy flax!"
They both rose up, pushed Wassilissa out of the
house and locked the door, crying: "Thou shalt
not come in till thou hast fetched the fire."

Wassilissa sat down on the doorstep, took the
tiny doll from one pocket and from another the
supper she had ready for it, put the food before it
and said: "There, my little doll, take it. Eat a
little and listen to my sorrow. I must go to the
hut of the old Baba-Yaga in the dark forest to

borrow some fire and I fear she will eat me. Tell me ! What shall I do ?"

Then the doll's eyes began to shine like two stars and it became alive. It ate a little and said : "Do not fear, little Wassilissa. Go where thou hast been sent. While I am with thee no harm shall come to thee from the old witch." So Wassilissa put the doll back into her pocket, crossed herself and started out into the dark, wild forest.

Whether she walked a short way or a long way the telling is easy, but the journey was hard. The wood was very dark, and she could not help trembling from fear. Suddenly she heard the sound of a horse's hoofs and a man on horseback galloped past her. He was dressed all in white, the horse under him was milk-white and the harness was white, and just as he passed her it became twilight.

She went a little further and again she heard the sound of a horse's hoofs and there came another man on horseback galloping past her. He was dressed all in red, and the horse under him was blood-red and its harness was red, and just as he passed her the sun rose.

That whole day Wassilissa walked, for she had

lost her way. She could find no path at all in the dark wood and she had no food to set before the little doll to make it alive.

But at evening she came all at once to the green lawn where the wretched little hut stood on its hens' legs. The wall around the hut was made of human bones and on its top were skulls. There was a gate in the wall, whose hinges were the bones of human feet and whose locks were jaw-bones set with sharp teeth. The sight filled Wassilissa with horror and she stopped as still as a post buried in the ground.

As she stood there a third man on horseback came galloping up. His face was black, he was dressed all in black, and the horse he rode was coal-black. He galloped up to the gate of the hut and disappeared there as if he had sunk through the ground and at that moment the night came and the forest grew dark.

But it was not dark on the green lawn, for instantly the eyes of all the skulls on the wall were lighted up and shone till the place was as bright as day. When she saw this Wassilissa trembled so with fear that she could not run away.

Then suddenly the wood became full of a terrible

noise ; the trees began to groan, the branches to creak and the dry leaves to rustle, and the Baba-Yaga came flying from the forest.   She was riding in a great iron mortar and driving it with the pestle, and as she came she swept away her trail behind her with a kitchen-broom.

She rode up to the gate and stopping, said :

"Little House, little House,
  Stand the way thy mother placed thee,
  Turn thy back to the forest and thy face to me !"

And the little hut turned facing her and stood still. Then smelling all around her, she cried : " Foo ! Foo ! I smell a smell that is Russian.   Who is here ?"

Wassilissa, in great fright, came nearer to the old woman and bowing very low, said : " It is only Wassilissa, grandmother.   My stepmother's daughters sent me to thee to borrow some fire."

" Well," said the old witch, " I know them. But if I give thee the fire thou shalt stay with me some time and do some work to pay for it. If not, thou shalt be eaten for my supper."   Then she turned to the gate and shouted : " Ho ! ye, my solid locks, unlock !   Thou, my stout gate, open !" Instantly the locks unlocked, the gate opened of

itself, and the Baba-Yaga rode in whistling. Wassilissa entered behind her and immediately the gate
shut again and the locks snapped tight.

When they had entered the hut the old witch
threw herself down on the stove, stretched out her
bony legs and said : "Come, fetch and put on the
table at once everything that is in the oven. I am
hungry." So Wassilissa ran and lighted a splinter
of wood from one of the skulls on the wall and
took the food from the oven and set it before her.
There was enough cooked meat for three strong
men. She brought also from the cellar *kwas*,
honey, beer and wine, and the Baba-Yaga ate and
drank the whole, leaving the girl only a little
cabbage soup, a crust of bread and a morsel of
sucking-pig.

When her hunger was satisfied, the old witch,
growing drowsy, lay down on the stove and said :
" Listen to me well, and do what I bid thee. To-
morrow when I drive away, do thou clean the yard,
sweep the floors and cook my supper. Then take
a quarter of a measure of wheat from my storehouse and pick out of it all the black grains and
the wild peas. Mind thou dost all that I have
bade ; if not, thou shalt be eaten for my supper."

Presently the Baba-Yaga turned toward the wall and began to snore and Wassilissa knew that she was fast asleep.   Then she went into the corner, took the tiny doll from her pocket, put before it a bit of bread and a little cabbage-soup that she had saved, burst into tears and said : " There, my little doll, take it.   Eat a little, drink a little, and listen to my grief.   Here I am in the house of the old witch and the gate in the wall is locked and I am afraid.   She has given me a difficult task and if I do not do all she has bade, she will eat me to-morrow.   Tell me ; what shall I do ? "

Then the eyes of the little doll began to shine like two candles.   It ate a little of the bread and drank a little of the soup and said : " Don't be afraid, Wassilissa the Beautiful.   Be comforted. Say thy prayers, and go to sleep.   The morning is wiser than the evening."   So Wassilissa trusted the little doll and was comforted.   She said her prayers, lay down on the floor and went fast asleep.

When she woke next morning, very early, it was still dark.   She rose and looked out of the window, and she saw that the eyes of the skulls on the wall were growing dim.   As she looked, the man dressed all in white, riding the milk-white horse, galloped swiftly around the corner of the hut, leaped the wall and disappeared, and as he went, it became quite light and the eyes of the skulls flickered and went out. The old witch was in the yard; now she began to whistle and the great iron mortar and pestle and the kitchen-broom flew out of the hut to her. As she got into the mortar the man dressed all in red, mounted on the blood-red horse, galloped like the wind around the corner of the hut, leaped the wall and was gone, and at that moment the sun rose. Then the Baba - Yaga shouted : " Ho ! ye, my solid locks, unlock ! Thou, my stout gate, open !" And the locks unlocked and the gate opened and she rode away in the mortar, driving with the pestle and sweeping away her path behind her with the broom.

When Wassilissa found herself left alone, she examined the hut, marvelling to find it filled with such an abundance of everything. Then she stood still, remembering all the work that she had been bidden to do and wondering what to begin first. But as she looked she rubbed her eyes, for the yard was already neatly cleaned and the floors were nicely swept, and the little doll was sitting in the storehouse picking the last black grains and wild-peas out of the quarter-measure of wheat.

Wassilissa ran and took the little doll in her arms. " My dearest little doll !" she cried. " Thou hast saved me from my trouble ! Now I have only to cook the Baba-Yaga's supper, since all the rest of the tasks are done !"

" Cook it, with God's help," said the doll, " and then rest, and may the cooking of it make you healthy !" And so saying it crept into her pocket and became again only a little wooden doll.

So Wassilissa rested all day and was refreshed ; and when it grew toward evening she laid the table for the old witch's supper, and sat looking out of the window, waiting for her coming. After awhile she heard the sound of horse's hoofs and the man in black, on the coal-black horse, galloped up to the wall-gate and disappeared like a great dark shadow, and instantly it became quite dark and the eyes of all the skulls began to glitter and shine.

Then all at once the trees of the forest began to creak and groan and the leaves and the bushes to moan and sigh, and the Baba-Yaga came riding out of the dark wood in the huge iron mortar, driving with the pestle and sweeping out the trail behind

her with the kitchen-broom. Wassilissa let her
in ; and the witch, smelling all around her, asked :
" Well, hast thou done perfectly all the tasks I
gave thee to do, or am I to eat thee for my
supper ?"

"Be so good as to look for thyself, grandmother,"
answered Wassilissa.

The Baba-Yaga went all about the place, tapping
with her iron pestle, and carefully examining everything. But so well had the little doll done its
work that, try as hard as she might, she could not
find anything to complain of. There was not a
weed left in the yard, nor a speck of dust on the
floors, nor a single black grain or wild-pea in the
wheat.

The old witch was greatly angered, but was
obliged to pretend to be pleased. "Well," she said,
"thou hast done all well." Then, clapping her
hands, she shouted ; " Ho ! my faithful servants !
Friends of my heart ! Haste and grind my
wheat !" Immediately three pair of hands appeared, seized the measure of wheat and carried it
away.

The Baba-Yaga sat down to supper, and
Wassilissa put before her all the food from the

oven, with *kwas*, honey, beer and wine. The old witch ate it, bones and all, almost to the last morsel, enough for four strong men, and then, growing drowsy, stretched her bony legs on the stove and said: " To - morrow do as thou hast done to-day, and besides these tasks take from my storehouse a half - measure of poppy - seeds and clean them one by one. Someone has mixed earth with them to do me a mischief and to anger me, and I will have them made perfectly clean." So saying she turned to the wall and soon began to snore.

When she was fast asleep Wassilissa went into the corner, took the little doll from her pocket, set before it a part of the food that was left and asked its advice. And the doll, when it had become alive, and eaten a little food and sipped a little drink, said : " Don't worry, beautiful Wassilissa ! Be comforted. Do as thou didst last night : say thy prayers and go to sleep." So Wassilissa was comforted. She said her prayers and went to sleep and did not wake till next morning when she heard the old witch in the yard whistling. She ran to the window just in time to see her take her place in the big iron mortar, and as she did so the man dressed all in red, riding on the blood-red horse, leaped over the wall and was gone, just as the sun rose over the wild forest.

As it had happened on the first morning, so it happened now. When Wassilissa looked she found that the little doll had finished all the tasks except the cooking of the supper. The yard was swept and in order, the floors were as clean as new wood, and there was not a grain of earth left in the half-measure of poppy-seeds. She rested and refreshed herself till the afternoon, when she cooked the supper, and when evening came she laid the table and sat down to wait for the old witch's coming.

Soon the man in black, on the coal-black horse, galloped up to the gate, and the dark fell and the eyes of the skulls began to shine like day; then the ground began to quake, and the trees of the forest began to creak and the dry leaves to rustle, and the Baba-Yaga came riding in her iron mortar, driving with her pestle and sweeping away her path with her broom.

When she came in she smelled around her and went all about the hut, tapping with the pestle; but pry and examine as she might, again she could see no reason to find fault and was angrier than ever.

She clapped her hands and shouted : " Ho ! my
trusty servants ! Friends of my soul ! Haste and
press the oil out of my poppy-seeds !" And instantly
the three pair of hands appeared, seized the measure
of poppy-seeds and carried it away.

Presently the old witch sat down to supper and
Wassilissa brought all she had cooked, enough for
five grown men, and set it before her, and brought
beer and honey, and then she herself stood silently
waiting. The Baba-Yaga ate and drank it all,
every morsel, leaving not so much as a crumb of
bread ; then she said snappishly : " Well, why dost
thou say nothing, but stand there as if thou wast
dumb ?"

" I spoke not," Wassilissa answered, " because I
dared not. But if thou wilt allow me, grandmother, I wish to ask thee some questions."

" Well," said the old witch, "only remember that
every question does not lead to good. If thou
knowest over much, thou wilt grow old too soon.
What wilt thou ask ?"

" I would ask thee," said Wassilissa, "of the men
on horseback. When I came to thy hut, a rider
passed me. He was dressed all in white and he
rode a milk-white horse. Who was he ?"

" That was my white, bright day," answered the
Baba-Yaga angrily. " He is a servant of mine, but
he cannot hurt thee.   Ask me more."

" Afterwards," said Wassilissa, " a second rider
overtook me.   He was dressed in red and the
horse he rode was blood-red.   Who was he ?"

" That was my servant, the round, red sun,"
answered the Baba-Yaga, " and he too cannot
injure thee," and she ground her teeth. "Ask me
more."

" A third rider," said Wassilissa, " came galloping up to the gate.   He was black, his clothes
were black and the horse was coal-black.   Who
was he ?"

" That was my servant, the black, dark night,"
answered the old witch furiously ; " but he also
cannot harm thee.   Ask me more."

But Wassilissa, remembering what the Baba-
Yaga had said, that not every question led to good,
was silent.

"Ask me more !" cried the old witch. "Why
dost thou not ask me more ?   Ask me of the three
pair of hands that serve me !"

But Wassilissa saw how she snarled at her and
she answered : "The three questions are enough

for me. As thou hast said, grandmother, I would not, through knowing over much, become too soon old."

"It is well for thee," said the Baba-Yaga, "that thou didst not ask of them, but only of what thou didst see outside of this hut. Hadst thou asked of them, my servants, the three pair of hands would have seized thee also, as they did the wheat and poppy-seeds, to be my food. Now I would ask a question in my turn: How is it that thou hast been able, in a little time, to do perfectly all the tasks I gave thee? Tell me!"

Wassilissa was so frightened to see how the old witch ground her teeth that she almost told her of the little doll; but she bethought herself just in time, and answered: "The blessing of my dead mother helps me."

Then the Baba-Yaga sprang up in a fury. "Get thee out of my house this moment!" she shrieked. "I want no one who bears a blessing to cross my threshold! Get thee gone!"

Wassilissa ran to the yard, and behind her she heard the old witch shouting to the locks and the gate. The locks opened, the gate swung wide, and she ran out on to the lawn. The Baba-Yaga seized

from the wall one of the skulls with burning eyes
and flung it after her : " There," she howled, " is
the fire for thy stepmother's daughters.   Take it.
That is what they sent thee here for, and may they
have joy of it !"

Wassilissa put the skull on the end of a stick
and darted away through the forest, running as fast
as she could, finding her path by the skull's glowing
eyes which went out only when morning came.

Whether she ran a long way or a short way, and
whether the road was smooth or rough, towards
evening of the next day, when the eyes in the skull
were beginning to glimmer, she came out of the
dark, wild forest to her stepmother's house.

When she came near to the gate, she thought,
" Surely, by this time they will have found some
fire," and threw the skull into the hedge ; but it
spoke to her, and said : " Do not throw me away,
beautiful Wassilissa ; bring me to thy stepmother."
So, looking at the house and seeing no spark of
light in any of the windows, she took up the skull
again and carried it with her.

Now since Wassilissa had gone, the stepmother
and her two daughters had had neither fire nor
light in all the house.   When they struck flint and

steel the tinder would not catch, and the fire they brought from the neighbours would go out immediately as soon as they carried it over the threshold, so that they had been unable to light or warm themselves or to cook food to eat. Therefore now, for the first time in her life, Wassilissa found herself welcomed. They opened the door to her and the merchant's wife was greatly rejoiced to find that the light in the skull did not go out as soon as it was brought in. "Maybe the witch's fire will stay," she said, and took the skull into the best room, set it on a candle-stick and called her two daughters to admire it.

But the eyes of the skull suddenly began to glimmer and to glow like red coals, and wherever the three turned or ran the eyes followed them, growing larger and brighter till they flamed like two furnaces, and hotter and hotter till the merchant's wife and her two wicked daughters took fire and were burned to ashes. Only Wassilissa the Beautiful was not touched.

In the morning Wassilissa dug a deep hole in the ground and buried the skull. Then she locked the house and set out to the village, where she went to live with an old woman who was poor and childless, and so she remained for many days, waiting for her father's return from the far-distant kingdom.

But, sitting lonely, time soon began to hang heavy on her hands. One day she said to the old woman: "It is dull for me, grandmother, to sit idly hour by hour. My hands want work to do. Go, therefore, and buy me some flax, the best and finest to be found anywhere, and at least I can spin."

The old woman hastened and bought some flax of the best sort and Wassilissa sat down to work. So well did she spin that the thread came out as even and fine as a hair, and presently there was enough to begin to weave. But so fine was the thread that no frame could be found to weave it upon, nor would any weaver undertake to make one.

Then Wassilissa went into her closet, took the little doll from her pocket, set food and drink before it and asked its help. And after it had eaten a little and drunk a little, the doll became alive and said: "Bring me an old frame and an old basket and some hairs from a horse's mane, and I will arrange everything for thee." Wassilissa hastened to fetch all the doll had asked for and when evening came, said her prayers, went to sleep, and in the morning she found ready a frame, perfectly made, to weave her fine thread upon.

She wove one month, she wove two months—all the winter Wassilissa sat weaving, weaving her fine thread, till the whole piece of linen was done, of a texture so fine that it could be passed, like thread, through the eye of a needle. When the spring came she bleached it, so white that no snow could be compared with it. Then she said to the old woman: "Take thou the linen to the market, grandmother, and sell it, and the money shall suffice to pay for my food and lodging." When the old woman had examined the linen, however, she said: "Never will I sell such cloth in the market-place; no one should wear it except it be the Tzar himself, and to-morrow I shall carry it to the Palace."

Next day, accordingly, the old woman went to the Tzar's splendid Palace and fell to walking up and down before the windows. The servants came to ask her her errand but she answered them nothing, and kept walking up and down. At length the Tzar opened his window and asked: "What dost thou want, old woman, that thou walkest here?"

"O Tzar's Majesty!" the old woman answered, "I have with me a marvellous piece of linen stuff, so wondrously woven that I will show it to none but thee."

The Tzar bade them bring her before him and when he saw the linen he was struck with astonishment at its fineness and beauty. "What wilt thou take for it, old woman?" he asked.

"There is no price that can buy it, Little Father Tzar," she answered; "but I have brought it to thee as a gift." The Tzar could not thank the old woman enough. He took the linen and sent her to her house with many rich presents.

Seamstresses were called to make shirts for him out of the cloth; but when it had been cut up, so fine was it that no one of them was deft and skilful enough to sew it. The best seamstresses in all the Tzardom were summoned but none dared undertake it. So at last the Tzar sent for the old woman and said: "If thou didst know how to spin such thread and weave such linen, thou must also know how to sew me shirts from it."

And the old woman answered: "O Tzar's Majesty, it was not I who wove the linen; it is the work of my adopted daughter."

" Take it, then," the Tzar said, " and bid her do it for me."

The old woman brought the linen home and told Wassilissa the Tzar's command : " Well I knew that the work would needs be done by my own hands," said Wassilissa, and, locking herself in her own room, began to make the shirts.   So fast and well did she work that soon a dozen were ready. Then the old woman carried them to the Tzar, while Wassilissa washed her face, dressed her hair, put on her best gown and sat down at the window to see what would happen.   And presently a servant in the livery of the Palace came to the house and entering, said : " The Tzar, our lord, desires himself to see the clever needlewoman who has made his shirts and to reward her with his own hands."

Wassilissa rose and went at once to the Palace, and as soon as the Tzar saw her, he fell in love with her with all his soul.   He took her by her white hand and made her sit beside him.   " Beautiful maiden," he said, " never will I part from thee and thou shalt be my wife."

So the Tzar and Wassilissa the Beautiful were married, and her father returned from the far-distant kingdom, and he and the old woman lived always with her in the splendid Palace, in all joy and contentment. And as for the little wooden doll, she carried it about with her in her pocket all her life long.

THE LITTLE HUMPBACKED HORSE

THE LITTLE HUMPBACKED HORSE

Across the wide sea-ocean, on the further side of high mountains, beyond thick forests, in a village that faced the sky, there once lived an old peasant who had three sons. The eldest, Danilo, was the most knowing lad in the place; the second, Gavrilo, was neither clever nor dull; and the youngest, who was named Ivan, was called a dullard, because while his brothers, after they had sowed their wheat and threshed it, drove to town and went merry-making, he cared to do nothing but lie in the corner on the stove and sleep. So the whole neighbourhood called him "Little Fool Ivan."

Now one morning when the peasant went to his stack, he found to his dismay that someone in the night had stolen some of the hay, so that evening he sent his eldest son to watch for the thief.

Danilo, accordingly, took his axe and his hay-fork and went to the field. On this night there was a biting frost and heavy snow, and he said to himself, " Why should I freeze myself stiff to save a little worthless fodder ?" So, finding a warm corner, he lay down, wrapped himself in his thick fur coat and went to sleep.

In the morning he saw that some of the hay had been stolen. He rolled himself well in the snow, went home and knocked at the door till his father let him in.

" Didst thou see the thief ?" asked the peasant.

" I heard him prowling not far off," answered Danilo ; " but I shouted and he dared not come nearer. However, I have had a terrible night, thou mayest be sure! It was bitter cold and I am frozen to the marrow !"

His father praised him, calling him a good son, and the next night sent his second son to watch.

So Gavrilo took his hatchet and his long knife and went to the field. Now on this night it was raining, and he said to himself, " They say my brother is cleverer than I, but I am at least knowing enough to take care of myself, and why should I stand all night wet to the skin for the sake of a little dried grass ?" So, having found a sheltered spot, he lay down, covered himself with his warm cloak and went to sleep.

In the morning he saw that more of the hay had been stolen. He went to a brook, poured water over his clothing so that it was drenched, went home and knocked at the door till it was opened.

" Didst thou see the thief ?" asked his father.

" I did," Gavrilo answered, " and laid hold of his coat and gave him such a beating that he will remember it. But the rascal tore away and ran so fast that I could not catch him. But I have had a night for my pains, I can tell you! The rain poured every minute and I am soaked to the bones !"

His father praised him likewise, calling him a brave fellow till he was as proud as a cock with five hens, and the next evening said to Little Fool Ivan : " Now, my son, it is thy turn to watch, but thou art such a simpleton thou canst not even keep the sparrows from the peas. It will be small use for thee to go."

However, Little Fool Ivan climbed down from the stove, put a crust of bread under his coat and went whistling off to the field. He did not lie down as his brothers had done, but went about the whole field, looking on every side, and when the moon rose he sat down under a bush, counted the stars in the sky and ate his crust with a good appetite.

Suddenly, just at midnight, he heard the neigh of a horse, and looking out from the bush he saw a wonderful mare, as white as snow, with a golden mane curled in little rings.

" So," said Little Fool Ivan to himself, " thou art, then, the thief of our hay ! Only come a little nearer and I will be on thy back as tight as a locust !" The mare came nearer and nearer and at last, choosing the right moment, Ivan leaped out, seized her tail and jumped on to her back, wrong side before.

The white mare's eyes darted forth lightning. She curled her neck like a snake, reared on her hind legs and shot off like an arrow. She raced over fields, she flew like a bird over ditches, she galloped like the wind along mountains and dashed through thick forests. But run as she would, and rear and snort as she might, she could not throw off Little Fool Ivan. He clung to her tail and stuck to her back like a burr.

At last, just as day was beginning to dawn, the

mare stopped and, panting, spoke to him with a human voice : " Well, Ivan," she said, " since thou canst sit me, it seems thou must possess me.   Take me home and give me a place to rest for three days. Only, each morning, just at sunrise, let me out to roll in the dew.   And when the three days are up, I will bear thee three such colts as were never heard of before.   Two of them will be Tzar's horses, of brown and grey, and these thou mayest sell if thou choosest.   But the third will be a little humpbacked stallion only three feet high, with ears a foot long, and him thou shalt neither sell for gold nor give as a gift to anyone whatsoever.   So long as thou art in the white world he shall be thy faithful servant.   In winter he will show thee how to be warm, and when thou dost hunger he will show thee where to find bread.   In return for these three colts, thou shalt release me and give me my freedom."

Little Fool Ivan agreed.   He rode the white mare home, hid her in an empty shepherd's corral, whose entrance he covered with a horse-cloth, and went home and knocked at the door till his brothers let him in.

When they saw him, they began to question

him. "Well, no doubt thou didst see the thief! Perhaps thou didst even catch him! Tell us."

"To be sure I did," he replied. "I jumped on the thief's back and laid hold of the villain's tail, and we ran a thousand *versts* or more. My neck was nearly broken in the end and ye may believe I am tired!" So saying he climbed on to the stove without taking off even his bark sandals, and went to sleep, while his brothers and his father roared with laughter at the story, not a word of which, of course, they believed.

Little Fool Ivan kept the white mare hidden from all other eyes. For three mornings he rose at daybreak and let her out to roll on the dewy meadow and on the fourth morning, when he went to the corral, he found beside her, as she had promised, three colts. Two were most beautiful to see; they were of brown and grey, their eyes were like blue sapphires, their manes and tails were golden and curled in little rings, and their hoofs were of diamond, studded with pearls. But the third was a tiny horse like a toy, with two humps on his back and ears a foot long.

Ivan was overjoyed. He thanked the white mare and she, released, curled her neck like a

snake, reared on her hind-legs and shot off like an
arrow.   Then he began to admire the three colts,
especially the little humpbacked one which frisked
like a dog about Ivan's knees, clapping his long ears
together from playfulness and dancing up and
down on his little hoofs.   He kept them hidden,
as he had the white mare, in the shepherd's corral,
letting them out each morning at sunrise to roll in
the dew and spending many hours petting them,
talking to them, currying their coats till they shone
like silver and braiding their golden manes.

Time went on (but whether it was three weeks or
three years that flew away matters little, since one
need not run after them) till it befell, one day, that
his eldest brother, Danilo, who had been to town
for a holiday, returned late at night and missing
his way in the darkness, stumbled into the shepherd's corral.   Hearing a sound, he made a light
and to his astonishment saw the three young horses.

" So—ho !" he thought.   " Now I understand
why Little Fool Ivan spends so much time in this
old corral !"   He ran to the house and woke his
brother Gavrilo.   " Come quickly," he said, " and
see what three horses our young idiot of a brother
has found for himself !"   And Gavrilo followed him

as fast as he could, straight across a nettle-field barefoot, since he did not wait to put on his boots.

When they came to the corral the two fine horses were neighing and snorting. Their eyes were burning like beautiful blue candles and their curling gold manes and tails and their hoofs of diamond and pearls filled the two brothers with envy. Each looked at them so long that he was nearly made blind of one eye. Then Danilo said :

" They say it takes a fool to find a treasure. But where in the white world could Little Fool Ivan have got these marvellous steeds ? As for thee and me, brother, we might search our heads off and we would find not even two *roubles !*" [1]

" That is true," answered Gavrilo. " We should have the horses, and not Little Fool Ivan. Now I have an idea. Next week is the Fair at the capital. Many foreigners will come in ships to buy linen and it is said that even Tzar Saltan will be there. Let us come here by night and take the horses thither and sell them. They will fetch a great price and we will divide it equally between us two. Thou knowest what a good time we could have with the money, and while we are slapping our

---

[1] One rouble = about two shillings English.

full purses and enjoying ourselves our dolt of an
Ivan will not be able to guess where his horses have
gone visiting. What sayest thou ? Let us shake
hands upon it."

So the two brothers agreed, kissed each other,
crossed themselves and went home planning how
to spend the money they should get for the horses.

When the next week came round, accordingly,
they said a prayer before the holy images, asked
their father's blessing and departed to the Fair.
When they had gone some distance, however, they
returned to the village secretly after nightfall, took
the two fine horses out of the corral and again set
out for the capital.

Next morning, when Ivan came to the corral, he
found to his grief that the beautiful pair had
vanished. There was left only the little humpbacked horse that was turning round and round
before him, capering, clapping his long ears together
and dancing up and down from joy. Ivan began
to weep salt tears. " O my horses, brown and
grey !" he cried ; " my good steeds with golden
manes ! Did I not caress you enough ? What
wretch—may he tumble through a bridge !—hath
stolen you away ?"

At this the humpbacked horse neighed and
spoke in a human voice : " Don't worry, little
master," he said. " It was thy brothers who took
them away and I can take thee to them. Sit on
my back and hold fast by my ears, and have a care
not to fall off !" So Little Fool Ivan sat on his
back, holding up his feet lest they drag on the
ground, and laid hold of his ears, and the pony
shook himself till his little mane quivered, reared on
his hind-legs, snorted three times and shot away like
an arrow, so fast that the dust curled under his feet.
And almost before Ivan had time to take breath,
he was *versts* away on the highroad to the capital.

When his brothers saw Little Fool Ivan coming
after them like the wind on his toy horse, they knew
not what to do. " For shame, ye rascals !" shouted
he as he overtook them. " Ye may be more clever
than I, but I have never stolen your steeds !"

" Our dear little brother !" said Danilo. " There
is little use denying. We took thy two horses, but
we did so with no thought of wrong to thee. As
thou knowest, this has been a poor season with our
crops and a bad harvest, and for despair I and
Gavrilo have been like to hang ourselves. When
we came by chance upon these two steeds, we

considered that thou hadst little knowledge of
bargaining and trading, and doubtless knew not
their worth, whereas we could get for them at
least a thousand *roubles* at the Fair. With this
money we could help our little father, as thou
wouldst wish, and we purposed to buy besides for
thee a red cap and new boots with red heels. So
if we have erred, do thou forgive us."

"Well," answered Little Fool Ivan, "thy words
sound fair enough. If this was your thought, go
and sell my two horses, but I will go with you."
So, though they wished him well strangled, the
two brothers had no choice but to take him with
them, and thus they came to the capital.

Now when they reached the market-place where
the traders were assembled, so wonderful were the
two steeds that the people swarmed about them,
buzzing like bees in a hive, till for the press no one
could pass either in or out, and there was great
commotion. Perceiving this the head-man sent a
crier who blew on a gold trumpet and shouted in
a loud voice: "O merchants and buyers! crowd
not, but disperse one and all!" But they would
not move from the horses. Then the head-man
rode out himself, in slippers and fur cap, with a

body of soldiers who cleared the way with their whips, so that he came to the middle of the market and saw the horses with his own eyes.

" God's world is wonderful !" he cried, rubbing his head. " What marvels doth it hold !" And bidding the crier proclaim that no buyer should buy them, he rode to the Palace, came to the presence of the Tzar, and told him of them.

The Tzar could not sit still for curiosity. He ordered his state-carriage and rode at once to the market, and when he saw the horses, tugging at their halters and gnawing their bits, with their eyes shining like sapphires, their curling golden manes, and hoofs of diamond and pearls, he could not take his eyes from them. He examined them on both sides, called to them with caressing words, patted their backs and stroked their manes, and asked who owned them.

" O Tzar's Majesty," said Little Fool Ivan, "I am their master."

" What wilt thou take for them ?" asked the Tzar.

" Thrice five caps full of silver," answered Ivan, " and five *roubles* beside."

" Good," said the Tzar, and ordered the money

HE CAME TO THE PRESENCE OF THE TZAR AND TOLD HIM OF THEM.

given him. Then ten grooms, with grey hair and
golden uniforms, led the pair to the royal stables.
On the way, however, the horses knocked the
grooms down, bit to pieces their bridles, and ran
neighing back to Ivan.

Then the Tzar called him to his presence, and
said : " It seems that my wonderful steeds will
obey only thee. There is no help but that I make
thee my Chief Equerry and Master of my Stables."
And he ordered the crier at once to proclaim the
appointment. So Little Fool Ivan called his
brothers Danilo and Gavrilo, gave to them the
fifteen caps full of silver, and the five *roubles* beside,
kissed them, bade them not neglect their father but
to care for him in his old age, and led the two
horses to the royal stables, while a great throng of
people followed, watching the little humpbacked
horse who went dancing after them up the street.

The telling of a tale is quick but time itself passes
slowly. Five weeks went by, while Ivan wore red
robes, ate sweet food and slept his fill. Each
morning at sunrise he took the horses to roll in the
dew on the open field, and fed them with honey and
white wheat till their coats shone like satin. But
the more the Tzar praised him, the more envious

many in the Court were of him.   As the saying is, one need not be rich only so he have curly hair and is clever; and because Little Fool Ivan had succeeded so easily people hated him, and the one who hated him most was the officer who had been the Tzar's Master of Horse before his coming. Each day this man pondered how he might bring about Ivan's ruin, and at night he would creep to the stables and lie hid in the wheat-bins, hoping to catch his rival in some fault.

When this failed, he went to all those Court officials who were envious of the new favourite and bade them hang their heads and go about with sorrowful faces, promising, when the Tzar asked the cause, to tell him what would ruin Little Fool Ivan. They did so, and the Tzar, noticing their sad looks, asked :

"O Boyars, why are ye cast down and crestfallen ?"

Then he who had given this counsel stood forth, and said : "O Tzar's Majesty ! not for ourselves do we grieve, but we fear thy new Master of the Stables is a wizard and an evil-doer and familiar with Black-Magic.   For he doth boast openly that he could fetch thee, if he chose, in addition to thy

two wonderful steeds, the fabled Pig with the
Golden Bristles and the Silver Tusks, with her
twenty sucklings, who live in the hidden valley of
the Land of the South."

Hearing this, the Tzar was wroth. " Bring
before me this wild boaster," he said, " and he shall
make good his words without delay !" Thereupon
they ran to the stables, where Little Fool Ivan lay
asleep, and kicked him wide awake and brought
him to the Tzar, who looked at him angrily, and
said : " Hear my command. If in three days thou
hast not brought hither, from the hidden valley of
the Land of the South, the Pig with the Golden
Bristles and Silver Tusks, together with her twenty
sucklings, I will deliver thee to an evil death !"

Little Fool Ivan went out to the stables weeping
bitterly. Hearing him coming, the little humpbacked horse began to dance and to flap its ears
together for joy, but as soon as he saw his master's
tears he almost began to sob himself. " Why art
thou not merry, little master ?" he asked. " Why
does thy head hang lower than thy shoulders ?"

Ivan embraced and kissed the little horse, and
told him the task the Tzar had laid upon him.
" Don't weep," said the pony ; " I can help thee.

Nor is this service so hard a one. Go thou to the
Tzar and ask of him a bucket of golden corn, a
bucket of silver wheat, and a silken lasso."

So Ivan went before the Tzar and asked, as he
had been bidden, for the wheat, the corn, and the
silken lasso, and brought them to the stables.
" Now," said the little humpbacked horse, " lie down
and sleep, for the morning holds more wisdom than
the evening."

Little Fool Ivan lay down to sleep, and next
morning the pony waked him at dawn. " Mount
me now," he said, " with thy grain and thy silken
rope, and we will be off, for the way is far."

Ivan put the silver wheat and the golden corn
into stout bags, slung them across the pony's neck,
and with his silken lasso wound about his waist,
mounted, and the little humpbacked horse darted
away like an eagle. He scoured wide plains, leaped
across swift rivers, and sped along mountain-ridges,
and after running without pause for a day and a
night, he stopped in a deep valley on the edge of a
dreary wood, and said : " Little master, this is the
Land of the South, and in this valley lives the Pig
with the Golden Bristles. She comes each day to
root in this forest. Take thou the golden corn and

the silver wheat and pour them on the ground in two piles, at some distance apart, and conceal thyself. When the Pig comes she will run to the corn, but the sucklings will begin to eat the wheat, and while the mother is not by, thou mayest secure them. Bring them to me and tie them to my saddle with the silken lasso and I will bear thee back. As for the Pig, she will follow her sucklings."

Little Fool Ivan did all as the little horse bade him. He entered the forest, put the corn and wheat in two piles, hid himself in a thicket near the latter, and rested till evening, when there came a sound of grunting, and the Pig with the Golden Bristles and Silver Tusks led her young into the forest. She saw the corn, and at once began to eat it, while the twenty sucklings ran to the wheat. He caught them, one by one, tied them with the silken lasso, and, hastening to the little horse, made them fast to his saddle-bow. Scarce had he mounted when the Pig perceived them, and seeing her sucklings borne away, came running after them, erecting her golden bristles and gnashing her silver tusks.

The little humpbacked horse sped away like a flash back along the road they had come, with the

Pig pursuing them, and, after running without stop for a night and a day, they arrived after dark at the Tzar's capital. Little Fool Ivan rode to the Palace courtyard, set down there the twenty suckling-pigs, still tied by the silken lasso, went to the stables and fell asleep.

In the morning the Tzar was greatly astonished to see that Little Fool Ivan had performed the task and was delighted to possess the new treasure. He sent for his Master of Horse and praised him and gave him a rich present, so that the envious ones thereat were made still more envious.

So, after some days, these came to the Tzar and said: "Thy Master of Horse, O Tzar's Majesty, doth boast now that the bringing of the wonderful Pig with her twenty sucklings was but a small service, and that he could, if he but chose, bring to thee the Mare with Seven Manes and her seven fierce stallions that graze on a green meadow between the crystal hills of the Caucasus."

Then, in more anger than before, the Tzar bade them bring Little Fool Ivan to his presence and said sternly: "Heed my royal word. If in seven days thou hast not brought hither from between the crystal hills of the Caucasus the Seven-Maned

Mare with her seven stallions, I will send thee
where the crows shall pick thy bones !"

Little Fool Ivan went weeping to the little
humpbacked horse and told him of the Tzar's new
command. " Grieve not, little master," said the
other ; " let not thy bright head droop. I can aid
thee. Nor is this service too hard a one. Go thou
to the Tzar and demand that he prepare at once a
stone stable with one door opening into it and
another opening out. Ask also for a horse's skin
and an iron hammer of twelve *poods*[1] weight."

Ivan obeyed. He demanded the stable, the
horse's skin and the iron hammer, and when all was
ready the little horse said : " Lie down and sleep
now, little master. The morning is wiser than the
evening." Little Fool Ivan lay down and slept,
and next morning at daybreak the pony waked
him. Ivan tied the horse's skin to the saddle-bow,
slung the hammer about his neck and mounted,
and the little humpbacked horse darted away like
a swallow, till the dust curled about his legs like a
whirlwind. When he had run three days and four
nights without rest, he stopped between two crystal
hills and said :

[1] One pood = about forty pounds English.

"Yonder lies the green meadow whereon each evening graze the Mare with Seven Manes and her seven fierce stallions. Take now thy horse's skin and sew me within it, and presently the mare will come and will set upon me with her teeth. While she rends the skin from me, do thou run and strike her between her two ears with thy twelve *pood* hammer, so that she will be stunned. Mount me then in haste, and thou mayest lead her after thee, and as for the seven stallions, they will follow."

So Little Fool Ivan sewed the little horse in the horse's skin, and when the mare with the seven stallions came, the stallions stood afar off, but the mare set upon him and rent the skin from him. Then Ivan ran and struck her with the iron hammer and stunned her, and instantly, holding her by her seven manes, leaped to the back of the little humpbacked horse.

Scarce had he mounted when the seven fierce stallions saw him and came galloping after them screaming with rage. But the little humpbacked horse was off like a dart back along the road they had come, and when they had travelled without stopping three nights and four days, they arrived at the Tzar's capital. Little Fool Ivan rode to the

stone stable that had been built, went in at one
door, and leaving therein the Mare with Seven
Manes, rode out of the other and barred it behind
him, and the seven stallions, following the mare,
were caught. Then Ivan went to his own place
and went to sleep.

When they reported to the Tzar that this time
also Little Fool Ivan had performed his task, the
Tzar was more rejoiced than before and bestowed
high rank and all manner of honours upon him,
till, for hatred and malice the envious ones were
beside themselves.

They conferred together and coming before the
Tzar, they said : " O Tzar's Majesty ! to bring thee
the mare and the stallions, thy Master of Horse
boasteth now, was but a small service, saying that,
if he willed, he could fetch thee from across three
times nine lands, where the little red sun rises, the
beautiful Girl-Tzar, whom thou hast so long desired
for thy bride, who lives on the sea-ocean in a golden
boat, which she rows with silver oars."

Then was the Tzar mightily angered. " Summon
this boaster again before me," he commanded, and
when Little Fool Ivan was come in, he bade him
bring him the lovely Girl-Tzar within twelve days

or pay the forfeit with his head. So, for the third
time, Ivan went weeping to the little humpbacked
horse and told him the Tzar's will.

"Dry thy tears, little master," said the other,
"for I can assist thee. This is not, after all, the
hardest service. Go thou to the Tzar and ask for
two handkerchiefs cunningly embroidered in gold,
a silken tent woven with gold thread and with
golden tent-poles, gold and silver dishes, and all
manner of wines and sweetmeats."

Ivan lost no time in obeying and when they
were ready brought them to the stables. "Lie
down and sleep now," said the little horse. "To-
morrow is wiser than to-day." Accordingly Little
Fool Ivan lay down and slept till the little horse
woke him at daybreak. He put all that had been
prepared into a bag and mounted, and the little
humpbacked horse sped away like the wind.

For six days they rode, a hundred thousand _versts_,
till they reached a forest at the very end of the
world, where the little red sun rises out of the blue
sea-ocean. Here they stopped and Ivan alighted.

"Pitch now thy tent on the white sand," said the
little horse. "In it spread thy embroidered handkerchiefs and on them put the wine and the gold

and silver plates piled with sweetmeats. As for
thee, do thou hide behind the tent and watch.
From her golden boat the Girl-Tzar will see the
tent and will approach it. Let her enter it and eat
and drink her fill. Then go in, seize and hold her,
and call for me." So saying, he ran to hide himself in the forest.

Ivan pitched the tent, prepared the food and
wine, and lying down behind the tent, made a tiny
hole in the silk through which to see, and waited.
And before long the golden boat came sailing
over the blue sea-ocean. The beautiful Girl-Tzar
alighted to look at the splendid tent and seeing the
wine and sweetmeats, entered and began to eat and
drink. So graceful and lovely was she that no tale
could describe her and Little Fool Ivan could not
gaze enough. He forgot what the little horse had
told him and he was still peering through the hole
in the silk when the beautiful maiden sprang up,
left the tent, leaped into her golden boat, and the
silver oars carried her far away on the sea-ocean.

When the little humpbacked horse came running
up, Ivan too late repented of his folly. " I am
guilty before thee!" he said. " And now I shall
never see her again!" and he began to shed tears.

" Never mind," said the little horse. " She will
come again to-morrow, but if thou failest next
time we must needs go back without her and thy
head will be lost."

Next day Little Fool Ivan spread the wines
and sweetmeats and lay down to watch as before;
and again the lovely Girl-Tzar came rowing in her
golden boat and entered the tent and began to
regale herself. And while she ate and drank Ivan
ran in and seized and held her and called to the
little horse. The girl cried out and fought to be
free, but when she saw how handsome little Fool
Ivan was, she quite forgot to struggle. He mounted and put her before him on the saddle, and the
humpbacked horse dashed away like lightning
along the road they had come.

They rode six days and on the seventh they
came again to the capital, and Little Fool Ivan—
with a sad heart, since he had fallen in love with
her himself—brought the lovely girl to the Palace.

The Tzar was overjoyed. He came out to meet
them, took the maiden by her white hand, seated
her beside him beneath a silken curtain on a
cushion of purple velvet, and spoke to her tender
words. " O Girl-Tzar, to whom none can be com-

pared!" he said. "My Tzaritza that is to be!
For how long have I not slept, either by night or
in the white day, for thinking of thine eyes!"

But the beautiful Girl-Tzar turned from him and
would not answer and again and again he tried his
wooing, till at length she said: "O Tzar, thou art
wrinkled and grey, and hast left sixty years behind
thee, while I am but sixteen. Should I wed thee,
the Tzars of all Tzardoms would laugh, saying that
a grandfather had taken to wife his grandchild."

Hearing this, the Tzar was angry. "It is true,"
he said, "that flowers do not bloom in winter and
that I am no longer young. But I am nevertheless a great Tzar."

Then she replied: "I will wed no one who hath
grey hairs and who lacks teeth in his head. If thou
wilt but grow young again, then will I wed thee
right willingly."

"How can a man grow young again?" he asked.

"There is a way, O Tzar," she said, "and it is
thus : Order three great caldrons to be placed in
thy courtyard. Fill the first with cold water, the
second with boiling water, and the third with boiling mare's-milk. He who bathes one minute in
the boiling milk, two in the boiling water, and three

in the cold water, becomes instantly young and so handsome that it cannot be told. Do this and I will become thy Tzaritza, but not otherwise."

The Tzar at once bade them prepare in the courtyard the three caldrons, one of cold water, one of boiling water, and one of boiling mare's milk, minded to make the test. The envious courtiers, however, came to him and said : " O Tzar's Majesty ! this is a strange thing and we have never heard that a man can plunge into boiling liquid and not be scalded. We pray thee, therefore, bid thy Master of Horse bathe before thee ; then mayest thou be assured that all is well." Now this counsel seemed to the Tzar good and he straightway summoned Little Fool Ivan and bade him prepare to make the trial.

When Ivan heard the Tzar's command he said to himself, " So I am to be killed like a sucking-pig or a chicken !" and he went sorrowfully to the stables and told the little humpbacked horse. " Thou hast found for me the Pig with the Golden Bristles," he said, " the Seven-Maned Mare, and the beautiful Girl-Tzar ; but now these are all as nothing and my life is as worthless as a boot-sole !" And he began to weep bitterly.

" Weep not, little master," said the little horse.
" This is indeed a real service that I shall serve
thee.   Now listen well to what I say.   When thou
goest to the courtyard, before thou strippest off
thy clothes to bathe, ask of the Tzar to permit them
to bring to thee thy little humpbacked horse, that
thou mayest bid him farewell for the last time.   He
will agree and when I am brought there I shall
gallop three times around the three kettles, dip my
nose in each and sprinkle thee.   Lose not a moment
then, but jump instantly in the caldron of boiling
milk, then into the boiling water, and last into the
cold water."

Scarcely had he instructed him when the Boyars
came to bring Ivan to the courtyard.   All the
Court Ministers were there to see and the place
was crowded with people, while the Tzar looked on
from a balcony.   The two caldrons were boiling
hot and servants fed the great fires beneath them
with heaps of fuel.   Little Fool Ivan bowed low
before the Tzar and prepared for the bath.

But having taken off his coat, he bowed again
and said : " O Tzar's Majesty ! I have but one
favour to ask.   Bid them bring hither my little
humpbacked horse that I may embrace him once

more for the last time!" The Tzar was in good
humour thinking he was so soon to regain his youth,
and he consented, and presently the little horse
came running into the courtyard, dancing up and
down and clapping his long ears together. But as
soon as he came to the three caldrons he galloped
three times round them, dipped his nose into each
and sprinkled his master; and without waiting a
moment Little Fool Ivan threw off his clothes and
jumped into the caldrons, one after the other.
And while he had been good-looking before, he
came from the last caldron so handsome that his
beauty could neither be described with a pen nor
written in a tale.

Now when the Tzar saw this, he could wait no
longer. He hastened down from the balcony and
without waiting to undress, crossed himself and
jumped into the boiling milk. But the charm did
not work in his case, and he was instantly scalded
to death.

Seeing the Tzar was dead, the Girl-Tzar came to
the balcony and spoke to the people, saying: "Thy
Tzar chose me to be his Tzaritza. If thou wilt, I
will rule this Tzardom, but it shall be only as the
wife of him who brought me from mine own!"

The people, well pleased, shouted : " Health to Tzar Ivan !" And so Little Fool Ivan led the lovely Girl-Tzar to the church and they were married that same day.

Then Tzar Ivan ordered the trumpeters to blow their hammered trumpets and the butlers to open the bins, and he made in the Palace a feast like a hill, and the Boyars and Princes sat at oak tables and drank from golden goblets and made merry till they could not stand on their feet.

But Little Fool Ivan, with his Tzaritza, ruled the Tzardom wisely and well, and grew never too wise to take counsel of his little humpbacked horse.

TZAREVICH IVAN, THE GLOWING BIRD AND THE GREY WOLF

TZAREVICH IVAN, THE GLOWING BIRD AND THE GREY WOLF

In a certain far-away Tzardom not in this Empire, there lived a Tzar named Wyslaff, who had three sons: the first Tzarevich Dimitry, the second Tzarevich Wassily, and the third Tzarevich Ivan.

The Tzar had a walled garden, so rich and beautiful that in no kingdom of the world was there a more splendid one. Many rare trees grew in it whose fruits were precious jewels, and the rarest of all was an apple-tree whose apples were of pure gold, and this the Tzar loved best of all.

One day he saw that one of the golden apples was missing. He placed guards at all gates of the garden; but in spite of this, each morning on counting, he found one more apple gone. At length he set men on the wall to watch day and night, and these reported to him that every night there came flying into the garden a bird that shone like the moon, whose feathers were gold and its eyes like crystal, which perched on the apple-tree, plucked a golden apple and flew away.

Tzar Wyslaff was greatly angered, and calling to him his two eldest sons, said : " My dear children, I have for many days sought to decide which of you should inherit my Tzardom and reign after me. Now, therefore, to the one of you who will catch the Glowing Bird, which is the thief of my golden apples, and will bring it to me alive, I will during my life give the half of the Tzardom, and he shall rule after me when I am dead."

The two sons, hearing, rejoiced, and shouted with one voice: " Gracious Sir! We shall not fail to bring you the Glowing Bird alive !"

Tzarevich Dimitry and Tzarevich Wassily cast lots to see who should have the first trial, and the lot fell to the eldest, Tzarevich Dimitry, who at evening went into the garden to watch. He sat down under the apple-tree and watched till midnight, but when midnight was passed he fell asleep.

In the morning the Tzar summoned him and said : " Well, my son, didst thou see the Glowing Bird who steals my golden apples ?" Being ashamed to confess that he had fallen asleep, however, Tzarevich Dimitry answered : " No, gracious Sir ; last night the bird did not visit thy garden."

The Tzar, however, went himself and counted the apples, and saw that one more had been stolen.

On the next evening Tzarevich Wassily went into the garden to watch, and he too fell asleep at midnight, and next morning when his father summoned him, he, like his brother, being ashamed to tell the truth, answered : " Gracious Sir, I watched throughout the night, but the Glowing Bird that steals the golden apples did not enter thy garden."

And again, Tzar Wyslaff went himself and counted and saw that another golden apple was missing.

On the third evening Tzarevich Ivan asked permission to watch in the garden, but his father would not permit it. " Thou art but a lad," he said, " and mightest be frightened in the long, dark night." But Ivan continued to beseech him till at length the Tzar consented.

So Tzarevich Ivan took his place in the garden, and sat down to watch under the apple-tree that bore the golden apples. He watched an hour, he

watched two hours, he watched three hours.
When midnight drew near sleep almost overcame
him, but he drew his dagger and pricked his thigh
with its point till the pain aroused him. And
suddenly, an hour after midnight, the garden
became bright as if with the light of many fires, and
the Glowing Bird came flying on its golden wings
to alight on the lowest bough of the apple-tree.

Tzarevich Ivan crept nearer, and as it was about
to pluck a golden apple in its beak he sprang
toward it and seized its tail. The bird, however,
beating with its golden wings, tore itself loose and
flew away, leaving in his hand a single long feather.
He wrapped this in a handkerchief, lay down on
the ground and went to sleep.

In the morning Tzar Wyslaff summoned him to
his presence, and said: " Well, my dear son, thou
didst not, I suppose, see the Glowing Bird ?"

Then Tzarevich Ivan unrolled the handkerchief,
and the feather shone so that the whole place was
bright with it. The Tzar could not sufficiently
admire it, for when it was brought into a darkened
room it gleamed as if a hundred candles had been
lighted. He put it into his royal treasury as a
thing which must be safely kept for ever, and

set many watchmen about the garden hoping to snare the Glowing Bird, but it came no more for the golden apples.

Then Tzar Wyslaff, greatly desiring it, sent for his two eldest sons, and said : " Ye, my sons, failed even to see the thief of my apples, yet thy brother Ivan, has at least brought me one of its feathers. Take horse now, with my blessing, and ride in search of it, and to the one of you who brings it to me alive will I give the half of my Tzardom." And the Tzareviches Dimitry and Wassily, envious of their younger brother Ivan, rejoiced that their father did not bid him also go, and mounting their swift horses, rode away gladly, both of them, in search of the Glowing Bird.

They rode for three days—whether by a near or a far road, or on highland or lowland, the tale is soon told, but the journey is not done quickly—till they came to a green plain from whose centre three roads started, and there a great stone was set with these words carved upon it :

" Who rides straight forward shall know both hunger and
    cold.
Who rides to the right shall live, though his steed be dead.
Who rides to the left shall die, though his steed shall live."

They were uncertain what to do, since none of the three roads promised well, and turning aside into a pleasant wood, pitched their silken tents and gave themselves over to rest and idle enjoyment.

Now when days had passed and they did not return, Tzarevich Ivan besought his father to give him also his blessing, with leave to ride forth to search for the Glowing Bird, but Tzar Wyslaff denied him, saying: " My dear son, the wolves will devour thee. Thou art still young and unused to far and difficult journeying. Enough that thy brothers have gone from me. I am already old in age, and walk under the eye of God; if He take away my life, and thou too art gone, who will remain to keep order in my Tzardom? Rebellion may arise and there will be no one to quell it, or an enemy may cross our borders and there will be no one to command our troops. Seek not therefore to leave me !"

In spite of all, however, Tzarevich Ivan would not leave off his beseeching till at length his father consented, and he took Tzar Wyslaff's blessing, chose a swift horse for his use and rode away he knew not whither.

Three days he rode, till he came to the green

plain whence the three ways started, and read the
words carved on the great stone that stood there.
" I may not take the left road, lest I die," he
thought, " nor the middle road, lest I know hunger
and cold.   Rather will I take the right-hand road,
whereon, though my poor horse perish, I at least
shall keep my life."   So he reined to the right.

He rode one day, he rode two days, he rode three
days, and on the morning of the fourth day, as he
led his horse through a forest, a great Grey Wolf
leaped from a thicket. "Thou art a brave lad, Tzarevich Ivan," said the Wolf, " but didst thou not read
what was written on the rock ?"   When the Wolf
had spoken these words he seized the horse, and
tearing it in pieces, devoured it and disappeared.

Tzarevich Ivan wept bitterly over the loss of his
horse.   The whole day he walked, till his weariness
could not be told in a tale.   He was near to faint
from weakness, when again he met the Grey Wolf.
" Thou art a brave lad, Tzarevich Ivan," said the
Wolf, " and for this reason I feel pity for thee.   I
have eaten thy good horse, but I will serve thee a
service in payment.   Sit now on my back and say
whither I shall bear thee and wherefore."

Tzarevich Ivan seated himself on the back of the

Wolf joyfully enough. "Take me, Grey Wolf," he said, "to the Glowing Bird that stole my father's golden apples," and instantly the Wolf sped away, twenty times swifter than the swiftest horse. In the middle of the night he stopped at a stone wall.

"Get down from my back, Tzarevich Ivan," said the Wolf, "and climb over this wall. On the other side is a garden, and in the garden is an iron railing, and behind the railing three cages are hung, one of copper, one of silver, and one of gold. In the copper cage is a crow, in the silver one is a jackdaw, and in the golden cage is the Glowing Bird. Open the door of the golden cage, take out the Glowing Bird, and wrap it in thy handkerchief. But on no account take the golden cage; if thou dost, great misfortune will follow."

Tzarevich Ivan climbed the wall, entered the iron railing and found the three cages as the Grey Wolf had said. He took out the Glowing Bird and wrapped it in his handkerchief, but he could not bear to leave behind him the beautiful golden cage.

The instant he stretched out his hand and took it, however, there sounded throughout all the garden a great noise of clanging bells and the twanging of musical instruments to which the golden cage was tied by many invisible cords, and fifty watchmen, waking, came running into the garden. They seized Tzarevich Ivan, and in the morning they brought him before their Tzar, who was called Dolmat.

Tzar Dolmat was greatly angered, and shouted in a loud voice: "How now! This is a fine, bold-handed Cossack to be caught in such a shameful theft! Who art thou, from what country comest thou? Of what father art thou son, and how art thou named?"

"I come from the Tzardom of Wyslaff," answered Tzarevich Ivan, "son of Tzar Wyslaff, and I am called Ivan. Thy Glowing Bird entered my father's garden by night and stole many golden apples from his favourite tree. Therefore the Tzar, my father, sent me to find and bring to him the thief."

"And how should I know that thou speakest truth?" answered Tzar Dolmat. "Hadst thou come to me first I would have given thee the Glowing Bird with honour. How will it be with thee now when I send into all Tzardoms, declaring how thou hast acted shamefully in my borders? However, Tzarevich Ivan, I will excuse thee this if thou wilt serve me a certain service. If thou wilt ride across three times nine countries to the thirtieth Tzardom of Tzar Afron, and wilt win for me from him the Horse with the Golden Mane, which his father promised me and which is mine by right, then will I give to thee with all joy the Glowing Bird. But if thou dost not serve me this service, then will I declare throughout all Tzardoms that thou art a thief, unworthy to share thy father's honours."

Tzarevich Ivan went out from Tzar Dolmat in great grief. He found the Grey Wolf and related to him the whole.

" Thou art a foolish youth, Tzarevich Ivan," said the Wolf. " Why didst thou not recall my words and leave the golden cage ?"

" I am guilty before thee !" answered Ivan sorrowfully.

" Well," said the Grey Wolf, " I will help thee. Sit on my back, and say whither I shall bear thee and wherefore."

So Tzarevich Ivan a second time mounted the Wolf's back. " Take me, Grey Wolf," he said, " across three times nine countries to the thirtieth Tzardom, to Tzar Afron's Horse with the Golden Mane." At once the Wolf began running, fifty

times swifter than the swiftest horse. Whether it
was a long way or a short way, in the middle of the
night he came to the thirtieth Tzardom, to Tzar
Afron's Palace, and stopped beside the royal stables,
which were built all of white stone.

"Now, Tzarevich Ivan," said the Wolf, "get down
from my back and open the door. The stablemen
are all fast asleep, and thou mayest win the Horse
with the Golden Mane. Only take not the golden
bridle that hangs beside it. If thou takest that,
great ill will befall thee."

Tzarevich Ivan opened the door of the stables
and there he saw the Horse with the Golden Mane,
whose brightness was such that the whole stall was
lighted by it. But as he was leading it out he saw
the golden bridle, and its beauty tempted him to
take it also. Scarcely had he touched it, however,
when there arose a great clanging and thundering,
for the bridle was tied by many cords to instruments of brass. The noise awakened the stablemen, who came running, a hundred of them, and
seized Tzarevich Ivan, and in the morning led him
before Tzar Afron.

The Tzar was much surprised to see so gallant a
youth accused of such a theft. "What!" he said.

"Thou art a goodly lad to be a robber of my horses. Tell me from what Tzardom dost thou come, son of what father art thou, and what is thy name?"

"I come from the Tzardom of Tzar Wyslaff," replied Tzarevich Ivan, "whose son I am, and my name is Ivan. Tzar Dolmat laid upon me this service, that I bring him the Horse with the Golden Mane, which thy father promised him and which is his by right."

"Hadst thou come with such a word from Tzar Dolmat," answered Tzar Afron, "I would have given thee the horse with honour, and thou needst not have taken it from me by stealth. How will it be with thee when I send my heralds into all Tzardoms declaring thee, a Tzar's son, to be a thief? However, Tzarevich Ivan, I will excuse thee this if thou wilt serve me a certain service. Thou shalt ride over three times nine lands to the country of the Tzar whose daughter is known as Helen the Beautiful, and bring me the Tzarevna to be my wife. For I have loved her for long with my soul and my heart, and yet cannot win her. Do this and I will forgive thee this fault and with joy will give thee the Horse with the Golden Mane and the golden bridle also for Tzar Dolmat. But if thou dost not serve me this service, then will I name thee as a shameful thief in all Tzardoms."

Tzarevich Ivan went out from the splendid Palace weeping many tears, and came to the Grey Wolf and told him all that had befallen.

"Thou hast again been a foolish youth," said the Wolf. "Why didst thou not remember my warning not to touch the golden bridle?"

"Grey Wolf," said Ivan still weeping, "I am guilty before thee!"

"Well," said the Wolf, "be it so. I will help thee. Sit upon my back and say whither I shall bear thee and wherefore."

So Tzarevich Ivan wiped away his tears and a third time mounted the Wolf's back. "Take me, Grey Wolf," he said, "across three times nine lands to the Tzarevna who is called Helen the Beautiful.' And straightway the Wolf began running, a hundred times swifter than the swiftest horse, faster than one can tell in a tale, until he came to the country of the beautiful princess. At length he stopped at a golden railing surrounding a lovely garden.

"Get down now, Tzarevich Ivan," said the Wolf; "go back along the road by which we came, and wait for me in the open field under the green oak-tree." So Tzarevich Ivan did as he was bidden. But as for the Grey Wolf, he waited there.

Toward evening, when the sun was very low and its rays were no longer hot, the Tzar's daughter, Helen the Beautiful, went into the garden to walk with her nurse and the ladies-in-waiting of the Court. When she came near, suddenly the Grey Wolf leaped over the railing into the garden, seized her and ran off with her more swiftly than twenty horses. He ran to the open field, to the green oak-tree where Tzarevich Ivan was waiting, and set her down beside him. Helen the Beautiful had been greatly frightened, but dried her tears quickly when she saw the handsome youth.

"Mount my back, Tzarevich Ivan," said the Wolf, "and take the Tzarevna in your arms."

Tzarevich Ivan sat on the Grey Wolf's back and took Helen the Beautiful in his arms, and the Wolf began running more swiftly than fifty horses, across the three times nine countries, back to the Tzardom of Tzar Afron. The nurse and ladies-in-waiting of the Tzarevna hastened to the Palace, and the Tzar sent many troops to pursue them, but fast as they went they could not overtake the Grey Wolf.

Sitting on the Wolf's back, with the Tzar's

beautiful daughter in his arms, Tzarevich Ivan began to love her with his heart and soul, and Helen the Beautiful began also to love him, so that when the Grey Wolf came to the country of Tzar Afron, to whom she was to be given, Tzarevich Ivan began to shed many tears.

" Why dost thou weep, Tzarevich Ivan?" asked the Wolf, and Ivan answered : " Grey Wolf, my friend ! Why should I not weep and be desolate ? I myself have begun to love Helen the Beautiful, yet now I must give her up to Tzar Afron for the Horse with the Golden Mane. For if I do not, then Tzar Afron will dishonour my name in all countries."

" I have served thee in much, Tzarevich Ivan," said the Grey Wolf, " but I will also do thee this service. Listen. When we come near to the Palace, I myself will take the shape of the Tzar's daughter, and thou shalt lead me to Tzar Afron, and shalt take in exchange the Horse with the Golden Mane. Thou shalt mount him and ride far away. Then I will ask leave of Tzar Afron to walk on the open *steppe*, and when I am on the *steppe* with the Court ladies-in-waiting, thou hast only to think of me, the Grey Wolf, and I shall come once more to thee."

As soon as the Wolf had uttered these words, he beat his paw against the damp ground and instantly he took the shape of the Tzar's beautiful daughter: so like to her that no one in the world could have told that he was not the Tzarevna herself. Then, bidding Helen the Beautiful wait for him outside the walls, Tzarevich Ivan led the Grey Wolf into the Palace to Tzar Afron.

The Tzar, thinking at last he had won the treasure he had so long desired as his wife, was very joyful, and gave Tzarevich Ivan, for Tzar Dolmat, the Horse with the Golden Mane and the golden bridle. And Tzarevich Ivan, mounting, rode outside the walls to the real Helen the Beautiful, put her before him on the saddle and set out across the three times nine countries back to the Tzardom of Tzar Dolmat.

As to the Grey Wolf, he spent one day, he spent two days, he spent three days in Tzar Afron's Palace, all the while having the shape of the beautful Tzarevna, while the Tzar made preparations for a splendid bridal. On the fourth day he asked the Tzar's permission to go for a walk on the open *steppe*.

"Oh, my beautiful Tzar's daughter," said Tzar

Afron, " I grant thee whatever thou mayest wish.
Go then and walk where it pleaseth thee, and perchance it will soothe thy grief and sorrow at parting from thy father." So he ordered serving-women
and all the ladies-in-waiting of the Court to walk
with her.

But all at once, as they walked on the open *steppe*,
Tzarevich Ivan, far away, riding with the real
Helen the Beautiful on the Horse with the Golden
Mane, suddenly bethought himself and cried :
" Grey Wolf, Grey Wolf, I am thinking of thee
now. Where art thou ?" At that very instant the
false Princess, as she walked with the ladies-in-waiting of Tzar Afron's Court, turned into the Grey
Wolf, which ran off more swiftly than seventy
horses. The ladies-in-waiting hastened to the
Palace and Tzar Afron sent many soldiers in
pursuit, but they could not catch the Grey Wolf
and soon he overtook Tzarevich Ivan.

" Mount on my back, Tzarevich Ivan," said the
Wolf, " and let Helen the Beautiful ride on the
Horse with the Golden Mane."

Tzarevich Ivan mounted the Grey Wolf, and the
Tzarevna rode on the Horse with the Golden Mane,
and so they went on together to the Tzardom of

Tzar Dolmat, in whose garden hung the cage with the Glowing Bird. Whether the way was a long one or a short one, at length they came near to Tzar Dolmat's Palace. Then Tzarevich Ivan, getting down from the Wolf's back, said :

" Grey Wolf, my dear friend ! Thou hast served me many services. Serve me also one more, the last and greatest. If thou canst take the shape of Helen the Beautiful, thou canst take also that of this Horse with the Golden Mane. Do this and let me deliver thee to Tzar Dolmat in exchange for the Glowing Bird. Then, when I am far away on the road to my own Tzardom, thou canst again rejoin us."

" So be it," said the Wolf and beat his paw against the dry ground, and immediately he took the shape of the Horse with the Golden Mane, so like to that the Princess rode that no one could have told one from the other. Then Tzarevich Ivan, leaving Helen the Beautiful on the green lawn with the real Horse with the Golden Mane, mounted and rode to the Palace gate.

When Tzar Dolmat saw Tzarevich Ivan riding on the false Horse with the Golden Mane he rejoiced exceedingly. He came out, embraced Ivan in the wide courtyard and kissed him on the mouth, and taking his right hand, led him into his splendid rooms. He made a great festival, and they sat at oak tables covered with embroidered cloths and for two days ate, drank and made merry. On the third day the Tzar gave to Tzarevich Ivan the Glowing Bird in its golden cage. Ivan took it, went to the green lawn where he had left Helen the Beautiful, mounted the real Horse with the Golden Mane, set the Tzarevna on the saddle before him, and together they rode away across the three times nine lands towards his native country, the Tzardom of Tzar Wyslaff.

As to Tzar Dolmat, for two days he admired the false Horse with the Golden Mane, and on the third day he desired to ride him. He gave orders, therefore, to saddle him, and mounting, rode to the open *steppe*. But as he was riding, it chanced that Tzarevich Ivan, far away with Helen the Beautiful, all at once remembered his promise and cried: " Grey Wolf, Grey Wolf, I am thinking of thee!" And at that instant the horse Tzar Dolmat rode threw the Tzar from his back and turned into the Grey Wolf, which ran off more swiftly than a hundred horses.

Tzar Dolmat hastened to the Palace and sent

many soldiers in pursuit, but they could not catch
the Grey Wolf, and soon he overtook the Horse
with the Golden Mane that bore Tzarevich Ivan
and the Tzarevna.

"Get down, Tzarevich Ivan," said the Wolf;
"mount my back and let Helen the Beautiful ride
on the Horse with the Golden Mane."

So Tzarevich Ivan mounted the Grey Wolf and
the Tzarevna rode on the Horse with the Golden
Mane, and at length they came to the forest where
the Wolf had devoured Tzarevich Ivan's horse.

There the Grey Wolf stopped. "Well, Tzarevich Ivan," he said, "I have paid for thy horse, and
have served thee in faith and truth. Get down
now; I am no longer thy servant."

Tzarevich Ivan got down from the Wolf's back,
weeping many tears that they should part, and the
Grey Wolf leaped into a thicket and disappeared,
leaving Tzarevich Ivan, mounted on the Horse with
the Golden Mane, with Helen the Beautiful in
his arms who held in her hands the golden cage in
which was the Glowing Bird, to ride to the Palace
of Tzar Wyslaff.

They rode on three days, till they came to the
green plain where the three ways met, and where

stood the great stone, and being very tired, the
Tzarevich and the Tzarevna here dismounted and
lay down to rest. He tied the Horse with the
Golden Mane to the stone, and lying lovingly side
by side on the soft grass, they went to sleep.

Now it happened that the two elder brothers of
Ivan, Tzarevich Dimitry and Tzarevich Wassily,
having tired of their amusements in the wood and
being minded to return to their father without the
Glowing Bird, came riding past the spot and found
their brother lying asleep with Helen the Beautiful
beside him. Seeing not only that he had found the
Glowing Bird, but a horse with a mane of gold and
a lovely Princess, they were envious, and Tzarevich
Dimitry drew his sword, stabbed Tzarevich Ivan to
death, and cut his body into small pieces. They
then awoke Helen the Beautiful and began to
question her.

"Lovely stranger," they asked, " from what
Tzardom dost thou come, of what father art thou
daughter, and how art thou named ?"

Helen the Beautiful, being roughly awakened,
and seeing Tzarevich Ivan dead, was greatly
frightened and cried with bitter tears : " I am the
Tzar's daughter, Helen the Beautiful, and I belong

to Tzarevich Ivan whom ye have put to a cruel
death. If ye were brave knights, ye had ridden
against him in the open field ; then might ye have
been victorious over him with honour ; but instead
of that ye have slain him when he was asleep.
What praise will such an act receive ?"

But Tzarevich Wassily set the point of his sword
against her breast and said : " Listen, Helen the
Beautiful ! Thou art now in our hands. We shall
bring thee to our little father, Tzar Wyslaff, and
thou shalt tell him that we, and not Tzarevich
Ivan, found the Glowing Bird, and won the Horse
with the Golden Mane and thine own lovely self.
If thou dost not swear by all holy things to say
this, then this instant will we put thee to death !"
And the beautiful Tzar's daughter, frightened by
their threats, swore that she would speak as they
commanded.

Tzarevich Dimitry and Tzarevich Wassily cast
lots to see who should take Helen the Beautiful
and who the Horse with the Golden Mane and
the Glowing Bird. The Princess fell to Tzarevich
Wassily and the horse and the bird to Tzarevich
Dimitry, and Tzarevich Wassily took Helen the
Beautiful on his horse and Tzarevich Dimitry took

the Glowing Bird and the Horse with the Golden
Mane and both rode swiftly to the Palace of their
father, Tzar Wyslaff.

The Tzar rejoiced greatly to see them. To
Tzarevich Dimitry, since he had brought him the
Glowing Bird, he gave the half of his Tzardom, and
he made a festival which lasted a whole month, at
the end of which time Tzarevich Wassily was to
wed the Princess, Helen the Beautiful.

As for Tzarevich Ivan, dead and cut into pieces,
he lay on the green plain for thirty days. And on
the thirty-first day it chanced that the Grey Wolf
passed that way. He knew at once by his keen
scent that the body was that of Tzarevich Ivan.
While he sat grieving for his friend, there came flying an iron-beaked she-crow with two fledglings,
who alighted on the ground and would have eaten
of the flesh, but the Wolf leaped up and seized
one of the young birds.

Then the mother Crow, flying to a little distance,
said to him : " O Grey Wolf, wolf s-son ! Do not
devour my little child, since it has in no way
harmed thee."

And the Grey Wolf answered : " Listen, Crow,
crow's-daughter ! Serve me a certain service, and

I will not harm thy fledgling. I have heard that across three times nine countries, in the thirtieth Tzardom, are two springs, so placed that none save a bird can come to them, which give forth, the one the water of death, and the other the water of life. Bring to me two bottles of these waters, and I will let thy fledgling go safe and sound. But if thou dost not, then I will tear it in pieces and devour it."

" I will indeed do thee this service, Grey Wolf, wolf's-son," said the Crow, "only harm not my child," and immediately flew away as swiftly as an arrow.

The Grey Wolf waited one day, he waited two days, he waited three days, and on the fourth day the she-crow came flying with two little bottles of water in her beak.

The Grey Wolf tore the fledgling into pieces. He sprinkled the pieces with the water of death and they instantly grew together ; he sprinkled the dead body with the water of life and the fledgling shook itself and flew away with the she-crow, safe and sound. The Grey Wolf then sprinkled the pieces of the body of Tzarevich Ivan with the water of death and they grew together ; he sprinkled the dead body with the water of life, and Tzarevich Ivan stood up, stretched himself and said : " How long I must have slept !"

· Yes, Tzarevich Ivan," the Grey Wolf said, " and thou wouldst have slept for ever had it not been for me. For thy brothers cut thee into pieces and took away with them the beautiful Tzar's daughter, the Horse with the Golden Mane and the Glowing Bird. Make haste now and mount on my back, for thy brother Tzarevich Wassily to-day is to wed thy Helen the Beautiful."

Tzarevich Ivan made haste to mount, and the Grey Wolf began running, swifter than a hundred horses, toward the Palace of Tzar Wyslaff.

Whether the way was long or short, he came soon to the city, and there at the gate the Grey Wolf stopped. " Get down now, Tzarevich Ivan," he said. " I am no longer a servant of thine and thou shalt see me no more, but sometimes remember the journeys thou hast made on the back of the Grey Wolf."

Tzarevich Ivan got down, and having bade the Wolf farewell with tears, entered the city and went at once to the Palace, where the Tzarevich Wassily was even then being wed to Helen the Beautiful.

He entered the splendid rooms and came where they sat at table, and as soon as Helen the Beautiful saw him, she sprang up from the table and kissed him on the mouth, crying : " This is my beloved, Tzarevich Ivan, who shall wed me, and not this wicked one, Tzarevich Wassily, who sits with me at table !"

Tzar Wyslaff rose up in his place and questioned Helen the Beautiful and she related to him the whole : how Tzarevich Ivan had won her, with the Horse with the Golden Mane and the Glowing Bird, and how his two elder brothers had slain him as he lay asleep and had threatened her with death so that she should say what they bade.

Tzar Wyslaff, hearing, was angered like a great river in a storm. He commanded that the Tzareviches Dimitry and Wassily be seized and thrown into prison, and Tzarevich Ivan, that same day, was wed to the Princess Helen the Beautiful. The Tzar made a great feast and all the people drank wine and mead till it ran down their beards, and the festival lasted many days till there was no one hungry or thirsty in the whole Tzardom.

And when the rejoicing was ended, the two elder brothers were made, one a scullion and the other a cowherd, but Tzarevich Ivan lived always with Helen the Beautiful in such harmony and love that neither of them could bear to be without the other even for a single moment.

MARIA MOREVNA

MARIA MOREVNA

FAR behind the blue sea-ocean, beyond the void places, in a city set in the midst of pleasant meads, there lived a Tzarevich whose name was Alexis, and he had three sisters, Tzarevna[1] Anna, Tzarevna Olga and Tzarevna Helena. Their mother had long been dead, and when it came the father's time to die he called the Tzarevich to him and put the three sisters in his care.

"Heed thou, my dear son, my counsel and command," he said. "Keep not thy sisters over-long with thee, nor delay their marriage, but who-ever may be first to ask the hand of either of them, to that one, if she consent, give her to be wed."

So the father died and was buried, and the Tzarevich and his sisters sorrowed, as was right, until time had dulled their grief. Before the Palace was a fenced garden, where, in the cool

---

[1] The daughter of a Tzar.

of the day, they used to walk together, and often as they walked the Tzarevnas would recall their father's words, and would say one to another : " I wonder which will be the first to be wed and what manner of lover will come wooing her."

One day as they strolled under the green trees, plucking red poppies, a great cloud, black as ink and shaped like a hawk, suddenly rose in the sky. "Let us hasten indoors, little sisters," said Tzarevich Alexis, "for a dreadful storm is about to break." They quickened their steps, and just as they entered the Palace a crash of thunder sounded, the roof split in two and a bright hawk came flying in. It alighted on the floor and was instantly transformed into a handsome youth.

" Greeting to thee, Tzarevich Alexis," said the youth. " Once I came to thy land as a visitor, but now I come as a suitor. I pray thee give me to wife thy little sister Anna."

" If she choose to wed thee, I shall not forbid," answered the Tzarevich. " How sayest thou, my sister ?"

So comely was the youth that Tzarevna Anna at once agreed, and the same day they were married and set out for the Hawk's Tzardom.

Hours grew into days, and days ran swiftly after one another till a year had vanished as if it had never been. Again one day Tzarevich Alexis went walking with his two sisters in the green garden, and again there rose up in the sky a cloud like a huge black eagle, with white lightnings flashing across it. " Let us seek shelter, little sisters," he said, " for a terrible whirlwind is rising." They hurried to the Palace, and as they entered it the thunder roared, the ceiling split in two and into the gap came flying an eagle. It alighted on the floor and instantly turned into a comely youth.

" Health to thee, Tzarevich Alexis," he said. " Heretofore I came to thy Tzardom as a visitor, but now I come to woo. Give me, I beseech thee, thy little sister Olga for my wife."

" If she so wills, then will I not deny thee," replied the Tzarevich. " What is thy mind, my sister ?"

The Hawk had been well-favoured, but the eagle was more handsome, and Tzarevna Olga lost no time in accepting him, so that same day the marriage was performed and the Eagle took her away to his own country.

Another year passed swiftly, and one day the

Tzarevich said : " Come, little sister, let us walk in
the green garden and refresh ourselves." As they
strolled among its flowers, again there rose the
cloud, shaped like a great black crow, and he said :
" Let us return with all speed to the Palace, for a
fierce tornado is upon us." They did so, but before
they had had time to sit down, there came a terrific
clap of thunder, the ceiling split and opened, and
into the room flew a crow. As it alighted it
became a graceful youth, who said :

" Prosperity to thee, Tzarevich Alexis ! In the
past I came to thy realm as a visitor, but now
I come seeking a wife. Grant me, I pray, thy little
sister Helena to wed."

" If she favour thy suit, I may not refuse her,"
returned the Tzarevich. " Wilt thou say 'aye,' my
sister ?"

The Hawk and the Eagle had been handsome but
the Crow was even more brilliant and splendid than
they and Tzarevna Helena agreed without delay.
The marriage took place at once and the Crow set
out with his bride for his own Tzardom.

Tzarevich Alexis, left solitary, was sad and lonely
and when a whole year had passed without sight or
sound of them, he said to himself : " I will go and

search for my three little sisters." So he called for his best horse and rode out into the white world.

He rode one day, he rode two days, he rode three days, till he came to a plain whereon a numerous army, with weapons broken and scattered, lay dead and dying. Sitting on his horse he cried aloud: " If there be one man here left alive, let him answer me. Who hath routed this great host ?" And one man whose life was yet in him replied where he lay: " These thousand stout warriors, O Tzarevich, were beaten by Maria Morevna, daughter of three mothers, granddaughter of six grandmothers, sister of nine brothers, the beautiful Tzar's daughter." And saying this he died.

Tzarevich Alexis rode on, till at length he came to a multitude of white tents pitched by the way, from the finest of which the lovely Maria Morevna came forth to greet him. " Health to thee, Tzarevich," she said. " Whither dost thou ride ? Is it by thine own will, or against it ?"

Tzarevich Alexis replied : " Brave men, Tzarevna, ride not anywhere against their will."

The beautiful Tzar's daughter was pleased with his answer. " Well," she said, " if thy business be not pressing, I pray thee stay awhile as my guest."

Tzarevich Alexis, nothing loath, dismounted and remained the guest of Maria Morevna, and before two days had passed they had fallen deeply in love with one another. She took him with her to her maiden Palace, where they were married with great rejoicing and there they lived many months together in happiness.

Now Maria Morevna was a warrior and at the end of this time there befell a rebellion on her border, so she called together her army and leaving Tzarevich Alexis in charge of her Palace, rode to the fight. "Guard and rule all things," she bade him, "only on no account open the door of the locked closet in my inner chamber."

The Tzarevich promised to obey her command, but she had not gone far on her way before his curiosity overmastered him. He went to the inner chamber, unlocked and opened the closet door, and there he saw an old man of huge form hanging from a beam, fettered with twelve riveted iron chains.

" Who art thou ?" asked the Tzarevich.

" I am Kastchey the Wizard," answered the old man. " Imprisoned by the father of Maria Morevna, I have suffered tortures here for ten

years. Have mercy on me, good youth, and fetch
me a little water to cool my parched throat!"

The Tzarevich pitied the Wizard. "A drink of
water can do no harm," he thought, and went and
fetched a jugful. The Wizard took it at a single
gulp. "My thirst is too great for a single draught
to quench," he said. "I pray thee give me
another, and when danger threatens thee I will
give thee thy life."

Tzarevich Alexis brought a second jugful and
this also Kastchey drank at a draught. "In mercy,
give me but one more," he pleaded, "and twice will
I give thee thy life when otherwise thou must
perish."

The Tzarevich brought him the third jugful,
which Kastchey also drank at a draught, but as
soon as he had swallowed it all the Wizard's former
strength returned; he strained at the twelve chains
and broke them asunder like rotten rope. "My
thanks to thee, Tzarevich!" he shouted. "Thou
art as likely now to possess thy Maria Morevna
again as to see thine own ears!" He flew out of
the window in a whirlwind, overtook the beautiful
Tzar's daughter on her way to the war, seized her
from the midst of her army and carried her away

across three times nine Tzardoms to his own land.

Tzarevich Alexis, seeing the misfortune his disobedience had wrought, wept bitterly and long. At length he wiped away his tears, and saying to himself, " Whatever may befall I shall not return until I have found Maria Morevna," he set out across three times nine Tzardoms.

He rode one day, he rode two days, and at dawn on the third day he came to a beautiful Palace of white stone whose roof shone like a rainbow. Before the Palace stood an oak-tree, on whose topmost branch perched a Hawk. As soon as it saw him, the Hawk flew down from the tree, alighted on the ground and became a handsome youth. " Welcome, my dear brother-in-law," he cried; " how hast God dealt with thee these past three years ?" The next moment Tzarevna Anna came running from the Palace, and kissing her brother began to ask him many questions and to tell him of what had befallen her.

Tzarevich Alexis spent three little days with them, at the end of which time he said: " I can remain no longer, but must go on my search for my wife, Maria Morevna."

His brother-in-law, the Hawk, answered: "It is a far journey. Leave with us thy silver spoon, that we may look upon it and be reminded of thee."

The Tzarevich left with him the silver spoon and rode on. He rode one day, he rode a second, and on the third, at daybreak, he came to a Palace of grey marble even finer than the Hawk's, whose roof was mother-of-pearl. Before it grew a fir-tree and on the tree perched an Eagle, which as soon as it saw him, flew down, alighted, and became a comely young man. "Hasten, wife," cried the Eagle, "our dear brother is coming!" And Tzarevna Olga came running from the Palace, kissed and embraced her brother and began to ply him with questions.

A second three little days Tzarevich Alexis spent with them and then said: "Farewell, my dear sister and brother-in-law, I go now to search for my wife, the beautiful Tzar's daughter."

"It is many *versts* to the Castle of Kastchey," said the Eagle, "and what shall we have to remember thee by? Leave with us thy silver fork."

He left with them the silver fork and rode away. A first day he rode, a second day he rode,

and on the third day, at sun-up, he found himself
approaching a third Palace of porphyry, roofed
with golden tiles, larger and more elegant than
the Hawk's and the Eagle's put together. In
front of the Palace stood a birch-tree on which
sat a Crow. The Crow flew down, alighted on the
ground and was transformed into a graceful youth.
" Come quickly, Tzarevna Helena," he cried, " our
little brother is coming !" Then Tzarevna Helena
came running from the Palace and met her brother
joyfully, embracing him with many questions.

With them also the Tzarevich abode three little
days, when he bade them farewell to continue his
search for his wife.

" Thy search may be in vain," said the Crow,
" for the Wizard Kastchey is very powerful and
cunning. We would have something to recall thee
to us. Leave with us thy silver snuff-box that we
may look on it often and know of thy welfare."

So Tzarevich Alexis left behind the silver snuff-
box and again set out. Whether he rode a long
way or a short way, by wet roads or dry, he came
at last to the Castle of Kastchey, where, walking
in the garden, he found his dear one, Maria
Morevna. When she saw him the beautiful Tzar's

daughter threw herself on his breast, weeping a
flood of tears. "O Tzarevich Alexis!" she cried,
"why didst thou disobey my command? Why
didst thou open the closet and loose the Wizard to
our hurt?"

"I am guilty before thee," answered the Tzarevich
sadly. "But remember not the old things which
are past. Come with me and let us fly, while
Kastchey is not to be seen. Perchance he will not
be able to overtake us." So without more ado he
took her up before him on the saddle and put his
good steed to its best pace.

Now that day the Wizard had gone hunting.
Toward evening he rode back to his Castle, when
suddenly his horse stumbled under him. Thereat
he rated it, crying: "Why stumblest thou, sorry
nag? Hast thou not been well fed, or dost thou
feel some misfortune?"

The horse replied: "Master, I feel a misfortune.
Tzarevich Alexis has been here and has carried
away thy Maria Morevna."

"Canst thou overtake them?" demanded the
Wizard.

"Thou mayest sow a measure of wheat," answered
the horse, "thou mayest wait till it is grown, harvest

and thresh it, grind the grain to flour, and of it
bake five ovens of bread to eat, and after that I
should be able to overtake them."

Kastchey put his horse to a gallop and easily
overtook Tzarevich Alexis. "Well," he said,
"when thou gavest me to drink, I promised on
occasion to give thee thy life. Therefore this time
I do not slay thee." Then taking Maria Morevna
from him, he returned to his Castle, leaving the
Tzarevich weeping.

Tzarevich Alexis wept a long time, but weeping
was of no avail and at length he dried his tears and
at daybreak on the morrow rode again to the
Wizard's Castle.

Kastchey was once more gone hunting, and the
Tzarevich, finding Maria Morevna in the garden,
said : " Come, mount with me and let us fly."

" Gladly would I," she answered, "but the Wizard
will overtake us, and I fear he will slay thee."

" At least we shall have had some hours together,"
said Tzarevich Alexis, and taking her up before
him, put spurs to his steed.

In the evening Kastchey returned from the hunt,
and as he neared his Castle his horse staggered.
"What dost thou, starveling hack !" he said.

" Art thou underfed, or dost thou scent some evil ?"

" I scent an evil, master," the horse answered. "Tzarevich Alexis has been here, and has borne away thy Maria Morevna."

"Canst thou overtake them ?" asked the Wizard.

The horse replied : " Thou mayest scatter a measure of barley, wait till it is high, cut it, thresh it, and of the grain brew beer. Thou mayest drink the beer till thou art tipsy and sleep till thou art sober, and still I should be able to overtake them."

The Wizard put his horse to a gallop and before long overtook Tzarevich Alexis. " Did I not tell thee," he said, " that thou shouldst as easily see thine own ears as again to possess Maria Morevna ? When thou gavest me water I promised to give thee twice thy life. Therefore, for this second time, I forbear to slay thee. But for the third time, beware !" So saying he took Maria Morevna and rode back to his Castle, leaving the Tzarevich weeping salt tears.

Tzarevich Alexis wept till his weeping was ended, and when the next day dawned, for the third time he rode to Kastchey's Castle.

This day also the Wizard was absent. He found

Maria Morevna and begged her to mount and fly with him. " Most gladly would I," she said, " but the Wizard will overtake us, and this third time he will not spare thee." But he answered : " If I cannot live with thee, I will not live without thee !" So he prevailed on her and took her up before him and spurred away.

When evening was come Kastchey rode home from his hunting, and as he neared his Castle his horse began to sway from side to side. "How now, thou beggarly cob !" he cried. " Dost thou lack fodder, or dost thou perceive some calamity ?"

"I perceive a calamity, master," replied the horse. " Tzarevich Alexis has been here and has ridden away with thy Maria Morevna."

" Canst thou overtake them ?" asked the Wizard.

And the horse answered : " Thou mayest strew a measure of flax-seed, wait till it is ripe, and pick, clean and card it. Thou mayest spin thread, weave cloth, sew a garment, and wear the garment into shreds, and even then I should be able to overtake them."

Kastchey made him gallop and at length overtook the Tzarevich. " Twice I gave thee thy life," he said, " but this third time thou shalt die." He killed his horse with a blow of the sword, dragged the Tzarevich to the Castle, put him in a cask barred and hooped with iron, and threw the cask into the sea-ocean, while Maria Morevna again he took to himself.

Now the Hawk, the Eagle and the Crow used often to look at the silver spoon, the fork and the snuff-box, and wonder how their brother-in-law fared in his search. One day, looking, they saw that the three pieces of silver were turning black, and they said to themselves: " Our little brother-in-law is in peril of his life." The Hawk flew at once to the Eagle, and together they sought the Crow. Having made their plan, the Crow flew to the west, the Eagle to the east, and the Hawk to the north, and after searching all day they met together to confer.

" I saw naught to remark," said the Hawk, " save a band of crows flying south."

" I saw and questioned them," said the Crow, " and they replied that they sighted something afloat on the sea-ocean."

" And I saw," said the Eagle, " what it was. It was a cask, barred and bound with hoops of iron."

"Brothers," said the Hawk, "let us see what the cask holds."

They flew together to where the cask floated, pulled it to shore, and with sharp beaks and claws picked and tore it apart, and in it to their delight they found their brother-in-law, the Tzarevich, safe and well. He told them all that had befallen him and begged their counsel.

When they had consulted together, the Crow said: "Our counsel is this. Kastchey's horse is a hundredfold swifter than any other, and for this reason, try as oft as thou wilt, he is sure to overtake thee. Find out where it was foaled, and perchance thou mayest obtain another as swift."

Tzarevich Alexis, having thanked them, set out again afoot for the Castle of the Wizard, where Maria Morevna wept tears of joy that he was still alive, and to her he said: "Find out, if thou canst, where Kastchey obtained his good horse, and tell me to-morrow."

So that night the beautiful Tzar's daughter said to Kastchey: "All things are open to thee, wise Wizard! Tell me, I pray, where was foaled thy marvellous steed which thrice overtook Tzarevich Alexis to his death?"

Kastchey said: "On the shore of the blue sea-ocean there is a meadow, and upon it there courses up and down a wonderful mare. Twelve hay-cutters reap the grass of the meadow, and as many more with rakes turn it. The mare follows them, devouring the grass they cut. When she bathes the sea rises in huge waves, and when she rubs her sides against the oak-trees they fall to the ground like sheaves of oats. Every month she brings forth a foal, and twelve fierce wolves follow her to devour them. Every three years the mare bears a she-colt with a white star on its forehead, and he who, at the moment it is born, snatches away this foal, fights off the wolves from it and brings it safely away, will possess a steed like to mine."

"Didst thou, O Kastchey," asked Maria Morevna, "gain thy horse by these means?"

"Not I," the Wizard answered. "Across three times nine lands, in the thirtieth Tzardom, on the further side of the River of Fire, there lives an old Baba-Yaga. She follows the mare and snatches away each she-colt which bears on its forehead the white star. She thus has many wonderful horses. I once spent three days tending them, and for

reward she gave me a little foal which became
the good horse I ride."

" But how didst thou cross the River of Fire ?"
asked Maria Morevna.

" As to that," replied the Wizard, " I have in my
chest a fine handkerchief. I have only to wave it
three times to my right side to have a strong bridge
so high that the fire cannot reach it."

Maria Morevna listened attentively, and when
Kastchey was asleep she took the fine handkerchief
from the chest, brought it to Tzarevich Alexis,
and told him all the Wizard had said.

The Tzarevich hastened away, crossed three
times nine countries, and in the thirtieth Tzardom
came to the River of Fire. By means of the
magic handkerchief he crossed it and went on
to find the old Baba-Yaga.

He walked one day, he walked two days, he
walked three days, without either food or drink.
When he was like to die from hunger he came
upon a bird with her fledglings. One of these he
caught, when the mother bird, flying near, said :
" Tzarevich, do not, I pray thee, eat my little one.
If thou wilt set it free, one day I will serve thee
a service."

The Tzarevich let the fledgling go, and soon
thereafter, in a forest, he found a wild-bee's hive.
He was about to eat the honey when the Queen-
Bee said: "Tzarevich, do not take the honey,
since it is food for my subjects. Leave it to
me, and one day, in return, I will serve thee a
service."

The Tzarevich left the honey, and went on till
he came to the sea-ocean, and on the sand he
caught a cray-fish. When he was about to eat it,
however, the cray-fish begged for its life. "Do
not eat me, Tzarevich," it said, "and one day I
will serve thee a service." So he let the cray-fish
go also, and went on his way, so tired and hungry
that he could scarcely crawl.

Whether he went a long way or a short way,
he came at length, at daybreak, in a forest, to the
hut of the old Baba-Yaga, turning round and
round on hens' legs. About the house were
planted twelve poles. On the tops of eleven
were men's heads, but the twelfth had none.

Tzarevich Alexis drew near and said:

> " Little hut, little hut !
> Stand the way thy mother placed thee,
> With thy back to the wood and thy face to me !"

And when the hut stood still facing him, he climbed up one of the hens' legs and entered. There lay the old witch on the stove, snoring.

The Tzarevich woke her. " Health to thee, grandmother!" he said.

"Health to thee, Tzarevich!" she answered. " Why hast thou come to me? Is it by thine own will, or by need?"

" By both," said Tzarevich Alexis. " I come to serve thee as herder, to graze thy she-horses and to earn a colt for my payment."

" Why shouldst thou not?" the Baba-Yaga said. " With me folk serve no round year, but only three days. If thou dost graze well my mares, I will give thee a steed fit for a hero. But if thou dost lose one of them, thy head shall be set upon my twelfth pole."

Tzarevich Alexis agreed. The old witch gave him food and drink, and ordered him to take her mares to the open field. He opened the stockade, but the instant they were free they whisked their tails and galloped off in different directions, so that they disappeared before he had scarce time to lift his eyes.

Then the Tzarevich began to weep and to

lament. He sat down on a stone and after weeping
for a long time fell asleep.

When the sun was setting a bird woke him by
pecking at his sleeve. "Rise, Tzarevich Alexis,"
said the bird; "the mares are all in the stockade.
I have served thee the service I promised when thou
didst loose my little fledgling."

He thanked the bird and went back to the
witch's hut, where the Baba-Yaga was shouting to
her sea-horses. "Why did ye come home?" she
cried to them, angrily.

"Why should we not?" they answered. "We
did thy bidding. We galloped far and further, but
flocks of birds came flying from the whole world
and came near to pecking out our eyes!"

"Well," she bade them, "to-morrow run not on
the meadow, but scatter throughout the thick
wood."

Tzarevich Alexis slept soundly. In the morning
the old witch sent him out again, saying: "Mind
thou losest none to-day, or thy head shall be put
upon my pole!"

He opened the stockade, but the moment they
were out the mares switched their tails and set off
running into the pathless woods. And again the

Tzarevich sat down on a stone and wept until he went to sleep.

Scarce, however, had the little sun begun to set behind the trees than a great bee came buzzing and woke him, and said : " Hasten, Tzarevich Alexis ; the mares are all in the stockade, and I have repaid thee for leaving my honey."

He thanked the bee and returned to the hut, where he found the Baba-Yaga again scolding her she-horses for returning.

" How could we help it ?" they replied. " We obeyed thy command and ran deep into the trackless forest, but thousands of angry bees came flying from the whole world and stung us till our blood came, and pursued us even here."

" Well," she told them, " to-morrow go neither to the meadow nor to the forest, but swim far out into the sea-ocean."

Again Tzarevich Alexis slept soundly, and when the next morning came the witch sent him a third time to graze her mares, saying : " Beware I miss no one of them at night, else shall thy head certainly be set upon my house-pole."

He loosed the mares from the stockade, but scarce were they outside when they flirted their

tails and galloping to the blue sea-ocean plunged
into the water up to their necks and swam until
they were lost to view. And the Tzarevich for a
third time sat him down on a stone to weep and so
fell asleep.

When the sun was low, he woke to find a cray-
fish nipping his finger. " Come, Tzarevich Alexis,"
it said, " the she-horses are all safe in their stalls,
and I have served thee my service in payment for
my life. Return now to the hut, but show not
thyself to the old witch. Go, rather, into the stable
and hide thyself behind the manger. In a corner
there thou wilt find a shabby little colt which is so
poor that it drags its hind-legs in the mire. When
midnight comes, take this little colt and depart to
thine own land."

The Tzarevich thanked the cray-fish, went back
to the hut and hid himself behind the manger.
And soon he heard the Baba-Yaga rating her she-
horses for returning.

" How could we remain in the water ?" they
answered. " We swam to the very middle of
the abyss, but hosts of cray-fish came creeping
from the whole sea-ocean, and with their claws
pinched the flesh from our bones, so that to escape

them we gladly would have run to the end of the white world."

The old witch waited and waited for the Tzare-vich's return, but at length she fell asleep. At midnight he saddled the shabby colt, led it from the stable and made his way to the River of Fire. He waved the Wizard's handkerchief three times to his right side and a strong high bridge sprang from bank to bank. He led his colt across it, and waving the handkerchief twice to his left side, the bridge shrank and became thin and narrow, till it was but one-third as high and one-third as strong.

Now at day-break the Baba-Yaga woke and missed the colt from the stable. She at once sprang into her iron mortar and started in pursuit, driving with her iron pestle and sweeping away her trail behind her with her kitchen-broom. She came to the River of Fire, and seeing the bridge, started to cross it. But she had scarce come to the middle when it gave way, and the old witch, falling into the flaming stream beneath, met her instant death.

As for Tzarevich Alexis, he grazed his colt twelve mornings at sunrise on the green meadow and it became a horse fit for a hero to ride. Then,

A BIRD WOKE HIM BY PECKING AT HIS SLEEVE

mounting, he galloped back to the Tzardom of
Kastchey, to the Wizard's Castle.   He found Maria
Morevna, and said : " Haste and mount before
me, for now I have a horse as good as Kastchey's !"
He took her on the saddle and rode off at full
speed.

In the evening when the Wizard returned, as he
neared his Castle, his horse fell upon one knee.
" What ! thou dawdling bag of bones !" he said.
" Dost stumble again ?   Art thou weak from
emptiness or dost thou smell some mishap ?"

" I smell a mishap, master," replied the horse ;
" Tzarevich Alexis has been here and has ridden
away with thy Maria Morevna."

" Canst thou overtake them ?" asked Kastchey.

" I cannot tell," the horse answered.   " The
Tzarevich has now for his steed my youngest
brother."

The Wizard put his horse at its best pace and
galloped in pursuit.   Whether he rode a long way
or a short way, by rough roads or smooth, at
length he overtook them and lifted his sword to cut
Tzarezich Alexis in pieces.

At that momemt the horse the Tzarevich rode
cried to the other: "O my brother! Why dost

thou continue to serve such an unclean monster? Cast him from thy back, and strike him with thy sharp hoofs." And the horse of Kastchey heard the counsel of his brother and threw his rider on the ground and lashed out with his hoofs so cruelly that the Wizard was forced to crawl back to his Castle on all fours.

Then Tzarevich Alexis mounted Kastchey's horse, and setting Maria Morevna on his own, they rode to visit his brothers-in-law, the Hawk, the Eagle and the Crow.

At each of the three Palaces they were received with rejoicing. " So thou hast gained thy Maria Morevna," they said. " Well, thou didst not take so much trouble for naught, since were one to search the whole world, he could find no other such a beauty!" And when their visits and feastings were ended they rode back to the Tzarevich's own Tzardom and lived happily together always and got all good things.

MARTIN THE PEASANT'S SON

MARTIN THE PEASANT'S SON

A LONG time ago, not in our day, beyond the trackless woods, beyond the desert sands, in a certain far Tzardom of a certain Empire, there lived an old peasant and his wife, who had one son called Martin. Time passed, and the peasant fell ill and died, and Martin and his mother grieved much and wept more than a little. Tears, however, could not avail, since they cannot bring back the dead, so the old woman began to plan by what means she and her son could live.

Now the peasant had left to his wife the sum of two hundred *roubles,* and though she disliked to begin so soon to spend it, they could not die of starvation. So when in a week's time they had eaten all the bread they had in store, she took a half of the sum and gave it to her son, saying: "There, my son, are a hundred *roubles.* Go to the neighbour's and borrow a horse and drive to town

149

to buy bread. With it we may somehow drag
through the winter, and when spring comes we can
search for work."

Martin borrowed the horse and went to town.
There, as he passed a butcher's shop, he saw the
street full of people and heard a great noise of
scolding. He stopped and found that the butchers
had caught a hunting-dog with drooping ears, and
having tied it to a post, were beating it with a stick,
while the poor dog, whining and crying, was struggling to tear himself free.

Martin ran to the butchers and stayed their
hands. "Brothers," he said, "why do ye treat so
unmercifully this poor dog?"

The butchers answered: "Why should we not
beat the wretched brute? He has spoiled for us a
whole side of beef!" And again they began be-
labouring him.

"Enough!" said Martin. "There is no profit for
you in that. Better sell him to me."

The butchers thought this an excellent jest.
"Very good," they replied. "Buy him if thou
wilt, but thou shalt give us a hundred *roubles* for
him."

"That I will," said Martin, and taking out his

hundred *roubles*, gave them to the butchers, untied the dog and took him home.   And all the way the dog wagged his tail and rubbed his head against his new master's hand as if to show he well understood that Martin had saved his life.

When Martin reached home, his mother asked :
" Little son, where is the bread thou didst buy ?"

" I bought none," he replied.

" What, then, hast thou purchased ?" asked she.

" I have bought a piece of good luck for myself," he answered, and showed her the dog, which he had named Jourka.[1]

" What luck is there in a dog, which must eat, even as we must ?" cried his mother.   " But what else didst thou buy ?"

" If I had had more money, I would have bought food," said Martin, " but the dog cost the whole hundred *roubles*."

Then the old woman began to upbraid him. " We have nothing to eat ourselves," she said, " for to-day I used the last scrapings of the bin to make a dry meal-cake.   To-morrow we shall not even have this !"

That night they ate the dry meal-cake while

---

[1] Growler.

his mother did not leave off her scolding, and
Martin broke his share in half and gave one piece
to the dog Jourka.

Next day the old woman took out the other
hundred *roubles*, and giving them to Martin, said :
" Here, little son, take the last of our money to
town and buy us bread, and mind thou dost not,
as before, waste it upon nothing."

Martin drove to town, and on his way to the
bake-shop he saw a crowd following a boy, who
had tied a cord about the neck of a cat with a
crooked tail, and was dragging her along the
street.

" Stop !" cried Martin.   " Where dost thou drag
that poor cat ?"

" I go to drown the rascally pest in the river,"
the boy replied.   " She has run off with a cake
from our table."

" No good can come to thee from that," said
Martin.   " Better sell her to me."

" Good," said the boy mockingly.   " Thou shalt
have her for a hundred *roubles*."

Martin spent no time in reflection.   He put
his hand into his breast, pulled out the money,
took the cat, put her into a bag and went home.

" Where is the bread thou didst buy, little son ?"
asked his mother.

" I bought none," he answered.

" What, then," the old woman asked, " didst
thou purchase ?"

So Martin took out the cat, which he had named
Vaska,[1] saying, I have bought this second piece
of good-luck for myself."

"Small luck in a cat, which must be fed," said
his mother.   " But what else didst thou purchase ?"

" If I had had more money," Martin replied, " I
would have bought food.   But I had to give the
whole hundred *roubles* for her."

At this the old woman flew into a passion.
" What a fool thou art!" she screamed.   " No
longer shalt thou live in this house!   Get thee
gone, and search for thy bread among strangers !"

So Martin left his home and went to a neigh-
bouring village to look for work, and wherever
he went Jourka the dog and Vaska the cat went
running after him.   At length he met a priest,
who asked, " Whither art thou going, good youth ?"

" To engage myself as a workman," replied
Martin.

---

[1] Puss.

"Come with me," said the priest. "I give no contract, but whoever labours for me three years will not be displeased with what I pay him."

Martin agreed and went with the priest, and laboured for him, without tiring, three summers and three winters. When it came time for his payment, the priest called him into his store-house and said: "Now, Martin, thou shalt receive the wage for thy service. Here are three bags, one filled with gold, one with silver, and one with sand. Take which thou wilt."

Martin looked at the bags and began to think. "If I take the gold," he said to himself, "I may buy what I will for a long time. If I take the silver, I shall be rich for a little time. If I take the sand, I shall be neither poorer nor richer than I am now. But who would take sand when he could get silver, or silver when he might have gold? There is surely some deeper reason hidden beneath this simple thing!" So, having reflected, he said: "By your leave, master, I choose the bag of sand."

"Well," said the other, "since thou despisest gold and silver, take it."

Martin hoisted up the heavy bag on to his back

and set out, followed by the dog with drooping
ears and the cat with the crooked tail, to find
another master and another service. He walked
a long way and he walked a short way, and the
bag grew heavier each minute, and the dog Jourka
and the cat Vaska followed after him wherever he
went. He came at length, in a thick dark wood
that seemed untrodden and asleep, to a green lawn,
and in the middle of it a fire had been kindled,
and in the fire, bound with twelve cords, sat a
maiden of such beauty that it could neither be
guessed nor dreamed of, but only told in a tale.

When the maiden saw him, she cried : "Good
youth, if thou wouldst get good luck for thyself,
haste and quench this flame !"

"To be sure," thought Martin, "it is better to
help a being in distress than to drag about such
a weight of useless sand, of which more can be
found anywhere," and untying the mouth of the
bag, he poured the sand on the flames and
extinguished them, and cut the twelve cords, and
set the maiden free.

"Who art thou, fair damsel ?" he asked.

"Thanks, good youth," said she. "I am
daughter to Tzar Zmey, the ruler of the Snake-

Tzardom, who is at war with Kastchey the Wizard.
He it was who prepared this hateful death from
which thou hast rescued me. But tell me, how
camest thou to bear on thy back the bag of sand?"

"It was my wage," he answered, "for three
years' service, and I chose it rather than silver
and gold."

"Then must it have been precious," she said.
"And yet, even so, I will richly repay thee." She
took a ring from her little finger and gave it to
him. "This is no ordinary ring," she said. "If
thou desirest anything, even though it be to wed
a Tzar's daughter, thou hast but to throw it from
one hand to the other. But beware to tell anyone
of it, else wilt thou bring upon thyself a great
misfortune." So saying, she struck her foot
sharply against the ground and instantly became
transformed into a snake, which darted away into
the forest.

"If all I want may be made to come so easily,"
thought Martin, "what is the need of seeking for
work?" and putting the ring on his finger, he
started back the way he had come. Whether it
was near or far, whether the journey was a long
one or a short one, he came at length to his native

Tzardom and to his own village, and finding his
old mother, who had repented with many tears
that she had sent him away in anger, they began
again to live together, with Jourka the dog and
Vaska the cat, without any sorrow. When they
had need of anything Martin had but to take off
his ring, throw it from one hand to the other, and
immediately twelve youths would appear, all alike
to the very hair and voice, saying: "What wilt
thou, Martin the peasant's son?" And he had
but to name what he desired, to have it straightway brought him.

Time passed and at length Martin made up
his mind to marry, and remembering what the
daughter of the Snake-Tzar had told him of the
ring, he said to himself, " Since I may have whomever I wish, I will wed the Tzar's daughter herself !"

He called his mother, therefore, and bade her go
to the Tzar and ask for the Tzarevna's hand ; but
the old woman besought him to give up his purpose. "It were far more suitable for thee, my
son," she said, "to marry a humble maiden.
Should I go to the Tzar with this mad invention
of thine, small doubt he would be angered and we
should both lose our heads."

"Never mind, little mother," he answered.
"Fear nothing. Surely, if I send thee on this
errand, thou mayest be bold enough to carry it.
Go and bring me the Tzar's answer, and come
not back without it."

So his mother hobbled off to the Tzar's Palace.
She went into the courtyard, and was half-way
up the stairway when the sentries seized her.
"What, beldame!" they said. "Wouldst thou go
where even mighty champions and valiant generals
may not pass without royal leave?"

"Ye blockheads!" scolded the old woman. "I
enter here on a fair errand! Who are ye, when I
come to arrange a marriage for my son with the
beautiful Tzarevna, to seize the skirt of my gown?"
And she fell to shrieking and upbraiding them
till the place had never known such a din and
even the Tzar heard it and came to the Palace
window.

Seeing the sentries dragging away an old woman,
he bade them let her in. They took their hands
from her, therefore, and she entered the room
where the Tzar sat with his sages and wise
counsellors, and first saying a prayer before the
holy pictures on the wall, saluted him.

"Well, old woman," he asked, "what wouldst thou with me?"

"O Tzar's Majesty!" she said, "I pray thee be not angered, but I have a merchant and thou hast merchandise. The merchant is my little son, Martin, who is the most clever lad in the world, and the merchandise is thy daughter, the beautiful Tzarevna. If thou wilt give her to him for wife, what a brave pair that will be!"

"Art thou mad, old woman?" shouted the Tzar.

"No, O Tzar," said she, "and if it please thee, give me thine answer."

The Tzar, thinking she had lost her wits, said: "Thou shouldst know, old woman, that a suitor for the hand of a Tzar's daughter should send rich gifts, precious things such as are not to be found in the royal treasury. Go, therefore, with God, till thou canst come in such manner, as is fitting." This he said, thinking easily to be rid of the matter.

So the old woman went back and gave the answer to her son. "And now," she said, "thou wilt give over this silly plan of thine."

Martin, however, went out of the cottage, threw his ring from one hand to the other, and instantly

the twelve youths, alike as twelve peas, appeared,
saying, "What wouldst thou, Martin the peasant's
son?" And he bade them bring, on twelve golden
trays, precious gifts fit for a Tzar, such as were not
to be found in the royal treasury. At once, dis-
appearing, they returned bearing all manner of
gold and silver work and jewels such as cannot be
described in words, and with these he sent his
mother to the Palace.

When the sentries reported to the Tzar that the
old peasant woman had returned thus laden, he
bade them admit her, and at the richness of the
gifts she brought could scarce believe his eyes.
When she again demanded the hand of his
daughter for her son, however, he called his
Ministers, asking: "What answer is a fitting one
to give? These are truly a king's gifts, and where
she has obtained them I cannot guess, but after all
her son is only a peasant, and it is not seemly that
a peasant wed a Tzarevna."

Then the Prime Minister, coming forward,
craved the Tzar's permission, and said to her:
"Since thy son, old woman, is, as thou hast said,
the cleverest lad in the world, let him build in one
round of the sun a splendid Palace beside this one,

with a bridge of crystal from one to the other.
Let the bridge be adorned with curious carvings,
and covered with embroidered carpets, and on
either side of it let there be a row of apple-trees
with fruit of silver and gold, and with birds-of-
paradise upon each branch. And near by let him
build a five-domed cathedral where, when they
are wed, he and the Tzarevna may receive the
marriage-crown. If thy son does this, then he
shall have the Tzar's daughter. If not, ye shall
both be beheaded."

The old woman went out from the Tzar's
presence to her son, weeping a flood of bitter tears.
" Did I not tell thee, my son," she said to Martin,
" to keep to thine own place ? But thou didst pay
no heed and now our heads are forfeit. To-morrow
we shall both be executed !"

" Weep not, little mother," he said, comforting
her ; " perhaps we shall not perish. Pray to God,
take a drink of *kwas*, and lie down to sleep ; we
may find more wisdom in the morning than in the
evening."

At midnight Martin rose, went outside the
cottage, threw the ring from one hand to the other,
and instantly the twelve youths appeared, saying :

"What wouldst thou, Martin the peasant's son?"
He bade them build the Palace as the Tzar's
Minister had demanded, and at once they rushed
away in different directions, returning with an
army of masons, carpenters, and foremen, and the
work began.

In the morning, the Tzar, going to his balcony,
saw to his surprise the Palace, the cathedral, the
crystal bridge with its costly carpets, and its trees
with silver and gold apples, all as had been required.
He sent, then, for his Ministers and Boyars, and
bade the beautiful Tzarevna prepare for her bridal.
"Little I thought," he said, "to behold thee wed
the son of a peasant, but I see not how it can be
avoided."

Meanwhile, at his own cottage, Martin, summoning by aid of the ring the twelve youths, demanded
a Boyar's dress, with an open carriage, richly
ornamented and drawn by six horses, and drove to
the cathedral. Thither also came the Tzar, with
all his Ministers, and with his daughter, washed,
powdered, rouged and clad in splendid Court robes,
and after the Mass, Martin the peasant's son and
the beautiful Tzarevna stood before the people and
were married.

The Tzar gave his daughter a rich marriage-
portion, bestowed high rank upon his son-in-law,
and made a festival for the whole realm, and the
newly-wedded pair began to live together in the
new Palace.

Now the Tzar's daughter was vain and proud,
and it angered her that she had been given, not to
a king nor to a Tzarevich, but to a simple peasant,
and she began to wish to be rid of her husband.
So she flattered him in every way and asked him
many wheedling questions in order to discover by
what means he was able to do such wonderful
things. For a long time Martin withstood her, but
one evening, when she had plied him with *vodka*[1]
and covered him with kisses and tempted him with
caressing words, he yielded and told her the secret
of the wonder-working ring.

As soon as he was asleep, his wife took the ring
from his finger, went to the balcony and threw it
from one hand to another, and instantly the twelve
youths appeared, saying, " What wouldst thou,
beautiful King's daughter ?" She bade them that
same hour to transport the Palace, the bridge and
cathedral, with herself, across three times nine

[1] Brandy.

lands to the thirtieth Tzardom, and as for her husband, to leave him lying on the meadow.

In the morning the Tzar went to his balcony, and looking, saw no longer either Palace, bridge or cathedral. He called messengers and sent them out, and running swiftly, they returned, saying: "O Tzar's Majesty! where yesterday were the splendid Palace and cathedral is now only a bare meadow, with thy son-in-law lying asleep in the middle of it. But thy daughter, the Tzarevna, is nowhere to be found."

In great wrath, the Tzar bade them bring Martin before him, and calling a council of his Boyars, demanded what he had done with the Palace and the Tzarevna. And when Martin could not answer, he gave orders to build a great stone column with but a single small window, and to wall him alive within it, without food or drink, till the Tzarevna be found. So the masons came and built the stone column and walled poor Martin in to die of starvation.

Now Jourka, the dog with drooping ears, had been away paying a visit, and returning on the third day, found what had happened to his master. He set off at once to the cottage of Martin's

mother, where he found Vaska, the cat, purring on
the stove. " O thou scoundrel Vaska," said he,
" who thinkest only to lie in warm places and to
scratch thyself! Knowest thou not that our
master is in danger of death? Hast thou forgot
how he paid a hundred *roubles* to save thy worthless life? But for him the worms would long ago
have eaten thee! Up, quickly! We must help
him in some way."

The cat leaped up from the stove and went with
the dog, and together they hastened to the stone
column, up which the cat was able to climb. Having
looked through the small window, she jumped to
the ground and said: " Our master is in evil case
and as helpless as a man with one leg tied to his ear.
He sits weeping, bemoaning the loss of a ring which
his wife hath taken from him, and left him to perish
of starvation. How can we get food for him?"

" Thou canst climb a wall, Vaska," said the dog,
" but all the same thou art a fool. I will tell thee
a way. We shall run about the town, and when
we meet a baker's boy with a tray, I shall roll under
his feet, so that he will stumble and drop the tray
from his head. Then do thou seize quickly a loaf
and make off with it, and carry it to the master."

The cat agreed, and going to the main street, they soon met a baker's apprentice with a tray. Jourka rushed under his feet, the boy staggered and dropped the tray, and from terror and fear lest the dog might be mad, ran away. The loaves scattered, and the cat, seizing one, carried it to the stone column, climbed to its top and pushed it through the little window. In the same way they frightened a peasant carrying *kwas* and brought Martin many a little bottle. So they took him one by one, loaves of white bread and rolls of brown, meats and provisions of all sorts, with *vodka* and *kwas* in abundance, sufficient for a whole year.

Then Jourka, the dog, said to the cat : " Thou saidst our master bemoaned the loss of his ring, which we may be sure is at the bottom of all his misfortune. His wife, who has taken it, has disappeared with the Palace. We have only to find the Palace, therefore, and we shall be near to finding the ring. Let us go in search of it without delay." Accordingly that same night they set out.

They went a long way and a short way, when they came to the blue sea-ocean, and there the cat mounted the dog's back and so they crossed to the

thirtieth Tzardom, and after a search, found the
Palace in which Martin had lived.

Then the dog said : " Thou, Vaska, creep into the
wine-cellar and keep thine eyes open, and when
the housekeeper sends for anything, haste and get
it for her.   I shall lie in the courtyard, and when
they send from the kitchen for fuel-wood, I shall
run and fetch it."   They did so, until one day the
housekeeper said : " I hear there is a cat with a
crooked tail in the wine-cellar which fetches whatever is required.   Bring her to me, and let her sleep
indoors."   And the cook said : " I hear there is
a dog in the courtyard which, as soon as I send
for wood, runs and fetches it.   Let him stay in the
kitchen at night."   So Jourka and Vaska had the
run of the house, and set themselves to discover
where the Tzarevna kept the wonder-working ring.
And soon they saw that the Tzarevna indeed had a
ring which she wore on her little finger, but by day
she never took it off, and try as they might they
could not succeed in getting into her sleeping
chamber.

Now when they had almost despaired of securing
it, the dog said to the cat : "The only thing that can
get at night into the Tzarevna's sleeping chamber

is a mouse. In this country is the Mouse-Tzardom. Let us go there and compel the Mouse-Tzar to aid us." They set out at once and soon arrived at the Tzardom of the Mice, where was no human being to be seen, but so many mice that it was impossible to count them. There they both fell upon the mice and began to kill them with teeth and claws and to pile their bodies in heaps, like sheaves.

Now this great slaughter produced terror throughout all the Tzardom, and at last, seeing so many of his subjects slain, the Mouse-Tzar himself came and saluting with his mustaches, prostrated himself humbly before the dog and cat. "O strong and powerful heroes!" he said, "have mercy on my wretched little people and make not my Tzardom perish! What service can I serve ye in return for our lives?"

Jourka, the dog, answered: "In this country is a Palace in which lives a beautiful Tzar's daughter. She has stolen from my master a ring which she wears on her little finger. Return to us the ring, or thy Tzardom shall be made empty and disappear."

The Mouse-Tzar called his subjects together,

great and small, and questioned them, whereupon
a mouseling came forward and said : " O Tzar's
Majesty, I know well the Palace and have often
been in the Tzarevna's sleeping chamber. She wears
the ring on her little finger by day, but at night,
when she lies down to sleep, she puts it in her
mouth."

" Bring it to me," said the Tzar, "and thou
shalt have the chief place of honour about my
person !"

The mouseling hastened to the Palace, and at
nightfall crept into the Tzarevna's bedroom, and
when she had fallen asleep, jumped to her pillow
and thrust his tail into her nostril. It tickled her
so that she sneezed and the ring flew out of her
mouth and rolled to the floor, where the mouseling
instantly seized it and carried it to the Mouse-Tzar,
who delivered it to the dog and cat.

Jourka and Vaska bade the Mouse-Tzar farewell
and prepared to return. " Give me the ring," said
the cat. " Thou, Jourka, must always be barking,
but I shall carry it in my mouth safer than one of
thine eyes." The cat put it in her mouth, therefore,
and they set out. When they came to the sea-
ocean, she mounted on Jourka's back, gripped his

coat with her claws, and the dog began to swim across.

He swam one hour, he swam two hours, he swam three hours, when a black, iron-beaked crow came flying and, alighting on the cat's head, began to peck it. Vaska was in sore trouble, for she dared not loosen her claws since she could not swim. Nor could she even so much as show her teeth to the crow lest she drop the ring. She endured it as long as she could, while the crow pecked till the blood came, until at length she could stand it no longer, and opening her mouth to defend herself, the ring dropped into the sea-ocean. The crow flapped away, and Jourka, as he swam, called out to know what was the matter.

Vaska dared not tell, lest the dog in anger drown her, so she said: "I did but stretch myself and yawn."

Presently they reached shore, when the cat instantly climbed a tree, from whose safe top she confessed her fault. "I am guilty before thee," she said. "A crow attacked me, and when I opened my mouth to drive it away, the ring fell into the sea-ocean."

"O miserable idiot!" cried the dog. "Lucky

for thee I did not know it before, else thou
shouldst have dived for it ! Thou shiftless mouth-
opener ! How shall we now appear before the
master ?"

"Well, Jourka," said the cat, "there is no
good in quarrelling. I have a plan, if thou wilt
make peace so that I may come down."

"The dog made peace, and coming down from
the tree, the cat said : "It is said that everything
that happens in the water is known to the lobsters.
Let us compel their Tzar to aid us."

So, running along the beach, they began to catch
and kill all lobsters, large and small, and to heap
the bodies as high as hay-stacks, so there fell great
fear in all the sea-ocean. At length, seeing so
many of his subjects slain, the huge Lobster-Tzar
came out of the water and prostrated himself
before the dog and cat. "Mighty heroes !" he said,
"I pray you cease to slaughter my people, and
whatsoever service ye will, that will I serve."

"Bring us," said Jourka, "a ring which we
dropped a little while ago in crossing the sea-ocean,
or thy whole Tzardom shall be made waste and
desolate."

The Lobster at once summoned his subjects, big

and little, and questioned them, when a little lobsterling came forward scarce a span long. "I saw the ring, O Tzar's Majesty!" he said. "The moment it fell into the sea-ocean, a pike-fish snatched and swallowed it before my eyes." Then the Lobster-Tzar bade his subjects depart into all parts of the sea-ocean and find the Tzar of the Pike-fish and order him to come before him, else would he declare unending war against him and all his kind.

They hastened into all waters, and when they had found the Tzar of the Pike-fish, they gave him the royal command, and with a great retinue of attendants he came swimming to where the Lobster-Tzar waited. He made his obeisance and the other said: "These two unconquerable heroes, my friends, but lately dropped into the sea-ocean a ring, which was swallowed by one of thy subjects. Find and bring hither that ring, else will I war against thee and waste and destroy thy whole Tzardom."

So the Tzar of the Pike-fish, since he feared the Lobster-Tzar, summoned all his people, and when they had gathered together small and great, he questioned them. And a tiny pike-fish swam forward, and said : " O Tzar's Majesty ! there is a pike I know who did swallow something this morning which disagreed with him so that he fell sick, and a little while ago he died."

The Tzar of the Pike-fish bade them bring the dead one, and as soon as they did so the dog fell upon it and began to devour it, beginning with the tail. Vaska, the cat, however, cunningly made a small hole in its side, stretched in her paw, found the ring and ran off with it, thinking : " While that glutton is dining, I shall run to our master and give him the ring, and he will think that I have found it unaided and will prefer me henceforth over Jourka."

The dog, not noticing Vaska's disappearance, continued to eat the fish until nothing remained save the head. " It is strange," he said to himself, "that my teeth have not yet found the ring." Missing his companion at that moment, however, he guessed what had happened, and ran in pursuit, barking: " Thou cheat ! Thou swindler ! If I but catch thee I shall tear thee into small pieces !"

Whether in a long time or a short time, he at length overtook the cat, but Vaska, coming to a birch-tree, climbed to its top and sat there with the ring in her mouth.

"Very well," said the dog, "thou wilt not sit there for the rest of thy life, and as for me I shall not stir from this spot."

For three days Vaska sat in the birch-tree, and during that time the dog did not take his eyes from her. Then the cat said: "Well, Jourka, there is no profit in quarrelling. Let us make peace, for if I do not come down our master cannot have his wonder-working ring."

So the dog made peace, and the cat came down from the tree, and together they hastened to their own capital, where Martin sat in the stone column waiting for death. The cat climbed the stone wall and pushed the ring through the little window so that it fell at Martin's feet.

Now for three days past Martin's food and drink had all been gone, and as it had been so long since he had seen his two faithful friends, he had concluded that some misfortune had befallen them and that he must die. When he saw the ring, however, and recognized it as the one he had lost, he rejoiced greatly, and at once, throwing it from one hand to the other, he summoned the twelve youths.

"What wilt thou, Martin the peasant's son?" they asked.

" Bring me," he answered, " food to eat and wine to drink, and since I have been sad, bring a band of musicians and let them play music so sweet that all who hear must stop and listen."

So the food and drink were brought and the music began to play while Martin gladdened his heart, and presently a messenger came to the Tzar and said: " O Tzar's Majesty, the prisoner, thy son-in-law, who should have been dead long ago, is surely a magician.   For from the column of stone in which he is prisoned there comes the noise of feasting and merriment and the sound of music, and a great concourse of people is gathered in the open square to listen."

The Tzar sent a herald to order them to disperse, but they could not move because of the music, which held even the herald spell-bound.   He sent, then, a troop of soldiers, but they also were compelled to stay and listen.   Finally the Tzar himself, with his attendants, left the Palace and went to the stone column.   But hearing the cunning music, he too found it impossible to leave the spot, so that he and his Court, his soldiers and well-nigh all the people of his capital, were forced to stand there till they were ready to faint from weariness.

At last, when night had come, the Tzar called to Martin, saying: " O my son-in-law, let thy music cease ! Tell me the meaning of these strange things, and thou shalt be forgiven !"

Martin caused the musicians to cease playing and called to the Tzar. " O Tzar's Majesty !" he said, " go to thy Palace and sleep. The morning will be wiser than the evening." So the troops dispersed the people, and the Tzar returned to the Palace. Then Martin, summoning the twelve youths, said : " Bring from the thirtieth Tzardom my Palace, with the five-domed cathedral and the crystal bridge, and let my unfaithful wife be brought also."

In the morning when the Tzar went to his balcony he saw all once more as it had been. He hastened to cross the crystal bridge to his son-in-law's Palace, where Martin met him, took his hand, and led him to his council-hall. There he recounted all that had befallen him at the hands of the Tzarevna, his wife. " Thus," he said, " did thy daughter by me, her husband. What, now, shall be her punishment ?"

The Tzar considered, and said : " She should be tied to the tail of a wild stallion and her body scattered in the deep ravines, but since she is my

SO THEY DWELT TOGETHER IN HAPPINESS ALWAYS.

daughter and thy wife, I beseech thee, my son-in-law, by thy forgiveness to make her ashamed of her folly and to take her to thee once more."

So Martin sent for his wife, who, having awaked to find her Palace in its old place, knew not what evil death awaited her, and he forgave her and took her again to wife.   And she was ashamed, and wept before him, and began to love him truly from that moment.

So they dwelt together in happiness always, but to his life's end Martin kept on his finger the wonder-working ring, and parted not with his two friends, Jourka the dog and Vaska the cat.

THE FEATHER OF FINIST THE FALCON

THE FEATHER OF FINIST THE FALCON

Once, in olden times, there was a merchant whose wife had died, leaving him three daughters. The eldest two were plain of face and hard of heart and cared for nothing but finery, while the youngest was a good housekeeper, kind-hearted, and so beautiful that it could neither be told in a tale nor written down with a pen.

One day, when the merchant set out for the Fair, he called his three daughters and asked: "My dear daughters, what do ye most desire me to buy for you?" The eldest answered: " Bring me a piece of rich brocade for a gown." The second said: " Bring me a fine scarf for a shawl." But the youngest replied: " Little father, bring me only a scarlet flower to set in my window."

The two sisters laughed at her request. " Little fool," they said, " what dost thou want of a scarlet

181

flower? Thou wouldst better ask for a new
apron." But she paid no heed and when the
merchant asked her again, she said : " Little father,
buy for me only the scarlet blossom."

The merchant bade them good-bye and drove to
the Fair, and whether in a short while or a long
while, he came again to his house. He brought the
rich brocade for the eldest daughter and the fine
scarf for the second, but he quite forgot to bring
the little scarlet flower. The eldest daughters were
so rejoiced at their gifts that he felt sorry for his
forgetfulness, and to comfort her, said to the
youngest: " Never mind, I shall soon go again to
the Fair, and shall bring thee a gift also." And she
answered : " It is no matter, little father ; another
time thou wilt remember." And while her sisters,
cutting and sewing their fine stuffs, laughed at her,
she was silent.

Time passed, and again the merchant made ready
to go to the Fair, and calling his daughters, he
asked : " Well, my daughters, what shall I buy for
you ?" The eldest answered, " Bring me a gold
chain," and the second, " Buy me a pair of golden
ear-rings ;" but the third said, "Little father, I want
nothing but a scarlet flower to set in my window."

The merchant went to the Fair and he bought for the eldest daughter the chain and for the second the ear-rings, but again he forgot the scarlet flower. When he returned and the eldest two daughters took joy in their golden jewellery, he comforted the youngest as before, saying : " A simple flower is no great thing. Never mind. When I go again I shall bring thee a gift." And again she answered : " It is no matter, little father ; another time perhaps I shall be luckier."

A third time the merchant made ready to go to the Fair, and called his three daughters and asked them what they most desired. The first answered, " Bring me a pair of satin shoes," the second said, "Buy me a silken petticoat ;" but the youngest said as before, " Little father, all my desire is for the scarlet flower to set in my window."

The merchant set out to the Fair, and he purchased the pair of satin shoes and the silken petticoat, and then he bethought himself of the scarlet flower and went all about inquiring for one. But search as he might, he could find not a single blossom of that colour in the whole town, and drove home sorrowful that he must disappoint his youngest daughter for the third time.

And as he rode along wondering where he might find the flower, he met by the roadside in the forest a little old man whom he had never seen, with a hooked nose, one eye, and a face covered with a golden beard like moss, who carried on his back a box.

" What dost thou carry, old man ?" he asked.

" In my box," answered the old man, " is a little scarlet flower which I am keeping for a present to the maiden who is to marry my son, Finist the Falcon."

" I do not know thy son, old man," said the merchant, " nor yet the maiden whom he is to marry. But a scarlet blossom is no great thing. Come, sell it to me, and with the money thou mayest buy a more suitable gift for the bridal."

" Nay," replied the little old man. " It has no price, for wherever it goeth there goeth the love of my son, and .I have sworn it shall be his wife's."

The merchant argued and persuaded, for now that he had found the flower he was loath to go home without it, and ended by offering in exchange for it both the satin shoes and the silken petticoat, till at length the little old man said : " Thou canst have the scarlet flower for thy daughter only on condition that she weds my son, Finist the Falcon."

The merchant thought a moment. Not to bring the flower would grieve his daughter, yet as the price of it he must promise to wed her to a stranger.

" Well, old man," he said, " give me the flower, and if my daughter will take thy son, he shall have her."

" Have no fear," said the little old man. " Whom my son woos, her will he wed!" and giving the box to the other, he instantly vanished.

The merchant, greatly disturbed at his sudden disappearance, hurried home, where his three daughters came out to greet him. He gave to the eldest the satin shoes and to the second the silken petticoat, and to see them they clapped their hands for delight. Then he gave to his youngest daughter the little box and said : " Here is thy scarlet flower, my daughter, but as for me, I take no joy of it, for I had it of a stranger, though it was not for sale, and in return for it I have promised that thou shalt wed his son, Finist the Falcon."

" Sorrow not, little father," said she. " Thou hast done my desire, and if Finist the Falcon will woo me then will I wed him." And she took out the

scarlet flower and caressed it, and held it close
to her heart.

When night came the merchant kissed his
daughters, made over them the sign of the cross
and sent them each to her bed. The youngest
locked herself in her room in the attic, took the
little flower from its box, and setting it on the
window-sill, began to smell it and kiss it and look
into the dark blue sky, when suddenly in through
the window came flying a swift, beautiful falcon
with coloured feathers. It lit upon the floor and
immediately was transformed into a young Prince,
so handsome that it could not be told in speech
nor written in a tale.

The Prince soothed her fright and caressed her
with sweet and tender words so that she began to
love him with such a joyful heart that one knows
not how to tell it. They talked—who can tell of
what ?—and the whole night passed as swiftly as an
hour in the daytime. When the day began to
break, Finist the Falcon said to her : " Each evening when thou dost set the scarlet flower in the
window I will come flying to thee. To-night, ere
I fly away as a falcon, take one feather from my
wing. If thou hast need of anything, go to the

steps under the porch and wave it on thy right side, and whatsoever things thy soul desireth, they shall be thine. And when thou hast no longer need of them, wave the feather on thy left side." Then he kissed her and bade her farewell, and turned into a falcon with coloured feathers. She plucked a single bright feather from his wing and the bird flew out of the window and was gone.

The next day was Sunday and the elder sisters began to dress in their finery to go to church. " What wilt thou wear, little fool ?" they said to the other. " But for thy scarlet flower thou mightst have had a new gown, instead of disgracing us by thy appearance."

" Never mind," she said ; " I can pray also here at home." And after they were gone she sat down at her attic window watching the finely-dressed people going to Mass. When the street was empty, she went to the steps under the porch and waved the bright feather to the right side, and instantly there appeared a crystal carriage with high-bred horses harnessed to it, coachmen and footmen in gold livery, and a gown embroidered in all kinds of precious stones. She dressed herself in a moment, sat down in the carriage, and away it went, swift as the wind, to the church.

When she entered, so beautiful she was that all the people turned to look at her. " Some high-born Princess has come !" they whispered to each other ; and in her splendid gown and head-dress even her two sisters did not recognize her as the one they had left in her little attic room. As soon as the choir began to sing the *Magnificat* she left the church, entered the crystal carriage and drove off so swiftly that when the people flocked out to stare there was no trace of her to be seen. As soon as she reached home she took off the splendid gown and put on her own, went to the porch, waved the bright feather to the left side and the carriage and horses, the coachmen in livery and the splendid gown disappeared, and she sat down again at her attic window.

When the elder sisters returned, they said : " What a beauty came to-day to church ! No one could gaze enough at her. Thou, little slattern, shouldst have seen her rich gown ! Surely she must have been a Princess from some other Province !"

Now so hastily had she changed her clothes that

she had forgotten to take out of her hair a diamond pin, and as they talked her sisters caught sight of it. " What a lovely jewel !" they cried enviously. " Where didst thou get it ?" And they would have taken it from her. But she ran to her attic room and hid it in the heart of the scarlet flower, so that though they searched everywhere they could not find it. Then, filled with envy, they went to their father and said : " Sir, our sister hath a secret lover who has given her a diamond ornament, and we doubt not that she will bring shame upon us." But he would not hear them and bade them look to themselves.

That evening when all went to bed, the girl set the flower on the window-sill, and in a moment Finist the Falcon came flying in and was transformed into the handsome Prince, and they caressed one another and talked together till the dawn began to break.

Now the elder sisters were filled with malice and spite and they listened at the attic door hoping to find where she had hidden the diamond pin, and so heard the voices. They knocked at the door, crying : " With whom dost thou converse, little sister ?"

" It is I talking to myself," she answered.

" If that is true, unlock thy door," they said.

Then Finist the Falcon kissed her and bade her farewell, and turning into a falcon, flew out of the window and she unlocked the door.

Her sisters entered and looked all about the room, but there was no one to be seen. They went, however, to their father and said: " Sir, our sister hath a shameless lover who comes at night into her room. Only just now we listened and heard them conversing." He paid no heed, however, but chided them and bade them better their own manners.

Each night thereafter the spiteful pair stole from their beds to creep to the attic and listen at the door, and each time they heard the sound of the loving talk between their sister and Finist the Falcon. Yet each morning they saw that no stranger was in the room, and at length, certain that whoever entered must do so by the window, they made a cunning plan. One evening they prepared a sweet drink of wine and in it they put a sleeping powder and prevailed on their sister to drink it. As soon as she did so she fell into a deep sleep, and when they had laid her on her bed, they fastened open knives and sharp needles upright on her window-sill and bolted the window.

When the dark fell, Finist the Falcon same flying to his love, and the needles pierced his breast and the knives cut his brilliant wings, and although he struggled and beat against it, the window remained closed. "My beautiful dearest," he cried, "hast thou ceased so soon to love me? Never shalt thou see me again unless thou searchest through three times nine countries, to the thirtieth Tzardom, and thou shalt first wear through three pair of iron shoes, and break in pieces three iron staves, and gnaw away three holy church-loaves of stone. Only then shalt thou find thy lover, Finist the Falcon!" But though through her sleep she heard these bitter words, still she could not awaken, and at last the wounded Falcon, hearing no reply, shot up angrily into the dark sky and flew away.

In the morning, when she awoke, she saw how the window had been barred with knives set cross-wise, and with needles, and how great drops of crimson blood were falling from them, and she began to wring her hands and to weep salt tears. "Surely," she thought, "my cruel sisters have made my dear love perish!" When she had wept a long time she thought of the bright feather, and ran to the porch and waved it to the right, crying : " Come to me, my own Finist the Falcon !" But he did not appear, and she knew that the charm was broken.

Then she remembered the words she had heard through her sleep, and telling no one, she went to a smithy and bade the smith make her three pair of iron shoes, and three iron staves, and with these and three church - loaves of stone, she set out across three times nine countries to the thirtieth Tzardom.

She walked and walked, whether for a short time or a long time the telling is easy but the journey is not soon done. She wandered for a day and a night, for a week, for two months and for three. She wore through one pair of the iron shoes, and broke to pieces one of the iron staves, and gnawed away one of the stone church-loaves, when, in the midst of a wood which grew always thicker and darker, she came to a lawn. On the lawn was a little hut on whose door-step sat a sour-faced old woman.

" Whither dost thou hold thy way, beautiful maiden ?" asked the old woman.

" O grandmother," answered the girl, " I beg for thy kindness ! Be my hostess and cover me from the dark night. I am searching for Finist the bright Falcon, who was my friend."

"Well," said the dame, "he is a relative of mine ; but thou wilt have to cross many lands still to find him. Come in and rest for the night. The morning is wiser than the evening."

The old woman gave the girl to eat and drink, a portion of all God had given her, and a bed to sleep on, and in the morning when the dawn began to break, she awoke her. "Finist, who flies as the falcon with coloured feathers," she said, "is now in the fiftieth Tzardom of the eightieth land from here. He has recently proposed marriage to a Tzar's daughter. Thou mayest, perhaps, reach there in time for the wedding-feast. Take thou this silver spindle ; when thou usest it, it will spin thee a thread of pure gold. Thou mayest give it to his wife for a wedding gift. Go now with God across three times nine lands to the house of my second cousin. I am bad-tempered but she is worse than I. However, speak her fair and she may direct thee further."

The girl thanked the old woman and bidding her farewell, set out again, though with a heavier heart, on her journey. She walked and walked,

whether for a short time or a long time, across green
steppe and barren wilderness, until at length, when
a second pair of iron shoes were worn through,
a second staff broken to pieces and a second stone
church-loaf gnawed away, she came one evening, on
the edge of a swamp, to a little hut on whose door-
step sat a second old woman, sourer than the first.

" Whither goest thou, lovely girl ?" asked the
dame.

" O grandmother," she answered, " grant me thy
kindness. Be my hostess and protect me from the
dark night. I seek my dear friend, who is called
Finist the Falcon, whom my cruel sisters wounded
and drove from me."

" He is a relative of mine," said the old woman,
" but thou wilt have to walk many *versts* further to
find him. He is to marry a Tzar's daughter and
to-day is her last maiden feast. But enter and
rest. The morning is wiser than the evening."

The old woman put food and drink before her
and gave her a place to sleep. Early on the
morrow she woke her. " Finist the Falcon," she
said, " lives in the fiftieth land from here. Take
with thee this golden hammer and these ten little
diamond nails. When thou usest them, the hammer

will drive the nails of itself. If thou choosest thou mayest give them to his wife for a wedding-gift. Go now with God to the house of my fourth cousin. I am crabbed but she is more ill-tempered than I. However, greet her with politeness and perhaps she will direct thee further. She lives across three times nine lands, beside a deep river."

The girl took the golden hammer and the ten little diamond nails, thanked the old woman and went on her way. She walked a long way and she walked a short way, and at last, when the third pair of iron shoes were worn through, and the third iron staff broken to pieces, and the third stone church-loaf gnawed away, she came, in a dark wood where the tops of the trees touched the sky, to a deep river and on its bank stood a little hut, on whose door-step sat a third old woman, uglier and sourer than the other two put together.

" Whither art thou bound, beautiful girl?" asked the dame.

" O grandmother," she answered, "grant me a kindness. Be my hostess and shield me from the dark night! I go to find Finist the Falcon, my dearest friend, whom my sisters pierced with cruel needles and knife-blades, and drove away bleeding."

" He is a relative of mine," said the old woman,
" and his home is not very far from here. But come
in and rest this night ; the morning is wiser than
the evening."

So the girl entered and ate and drank what the
old woman gave her, and slept till daybreak, when
the other woke her and said : " Finist the Falcon
with coloured feathers is now in the next Tzardom
from here, beside the blue sea-ocean, where he stays
at the Palace, for in three days he is to marry the
Tzar's daughter. Go now with God and take
with thee this golden saucer and this little diamond
ball. Set the ball on the plate and it will roll of
itself. Mayhap thou wilt wish to give them as a
wedding-gift to his bride."

She thanked the old woman and started again on
her way, and in the afternoon she came to the blue
sea-ocean spreading wide and free before her, and
beside it she saw a Palace with high towers of white
stone whose golden tops were glowing like fire.
Near the Palace a black serving-wench was washing
a piece of cloth in the sea, whose waves it tinged
with red, and the girl said : " What is it thou dost
cleanse ?"

The servant answered : " It is a shirt of Finist

the Falcon, who in three days will wed my mistress, but it is so stained with blood that I can by no means make it clean." The girl thought, " It is a garment my beloved wore after he was so cruelly wounded by the knives in my window !" And taking it from the other's hands, she began to weep over it, so that the tears washed away every stain and the shirt was as white as snow.

The black serving-woman took the shirt back to the Tzar's daughter, who asked her how she had so easily cleansed it, and the woman answered that a beautiful maiden, alone on the sea-sand, had wept over it till her tears had made it white. " This is, in truth, a remarkable thing," said the Tzar's daughter ; " I would see this girl whose tears can wash away such stains." And summoning her maids and nurses and attendants, she went walking along the shore.

Presently she came where the merchant's daughter sat alone on the soft sand gazing sorrowfully out over the blue sea-ocean, and she accosted her and said : " What grief hast thou that thy tears can wash away blood ?"

" I grieve," answered the girl, "because I so long to see the beautiful Finist the Falcon."

Then the Tzar's daughter, being very prideful, tossed her head, saying: " Is that all ? Go to the Palace kitchen, and I will let thee serve there ; perchance as payment thou mayest catch a glimpse of him as he dines."

So the merchant's daughter entered the Palace and was given a humble place among the servants, and when Finist the Falcon sat him down to dine, she put the food before him with her own hands. But he, moody and longing for his lost love, sat without raising his eyes and never so much as saw her or guessed her presence.

After dinner, sad and lonely, she went out to the sea-beach and sitting down on the soft sand, took her little silver spindle and began to draw out a thread. And in the cool of the evening the Tzar's daughter, with her attendants, came walking there and seeing that the thread that came from the spindle was of pure gold, said to her : " Maiden, wilt thou sell me that plaything ?"

" If thou wilt buy it at my price," answered the girl.

" And what is thy price ?" asked the Tzar's daughter.

" Let me sit through one night by the side of thy promised husband," said the girl.

Now the Tzar's daughter was cold and deceitful, and desired Finist the Falcon, not because she loved him, but because of his beauty and her own pride. " There can be no harm in that," she thought, " for I will put in his hair an enchanted pin, by reason of which he will not waken, and with the spindle I can cover myself and my little mother with gold." So she agreed, and that night when Finist the Falcon was asleep, she put in his hair the enchanted pin, brought the girl to his room, and said : " Give me now the spindle, and in return thou mayest sit here till daybreak and keep the flies from him."

All night the girl bent over the bed where the handsome youth lay sleeping, and wept bitter tears. " Awake and rise, Finist, my bright Falcon," she cried. " I have come at last to thee. I have left my little father and my cruel sisters, and I have searched through three times nine lands and a hundred Tzardoms for thee, my beloved !" But Finist slept on and heard nothing, and so the whole long night passed away.

And with the dawn came the Tzar's daughter and sent the girl back to the kitchen, and she took away the enchanted pin so that Finist the Falcon should awaken.

When he came from his chamber, the Tzar's daughter said to him : " Hast thou rested well, and art thou refreshed ?"

He answered: "I slept, but it seemed to me that someone was beside me all night, weeping and lamenting and beseeching me to awaken, yet I could not arouse myself, and because of that my head is heavy."

And she said: " Thou wert but dreaming ! No one has been beside thee !" So Finist the Falcon called for his horse and betook himself to the open *steppe* a-hunting.

As it happened before, so it befell that day also. Finist the Falcon had no eyes for the girl who waited on him at table, and in the evening, sad and sorrowful, she went out to the blue sea-ocean, and sitting down on the soft sand, took out the golden hammer and the ten diamond nails and began to play with them. A little later the Tzar's daughter, with her maids and attendants, came walking along the beach, and seeing how the hammer drove the nails by itself, coveted the plaything and desired to buy it.

" It shall be thine," said the girl, " if thou wilt pay me my price."

SHE CAME TO THE BLUE SEA-OCEAN . . . . AND BESIDE IT SHE SAW A PALACE.

" And what is the price?" asked the Tzar's daughter.

" Let me watch a second night beside the bed of thy promised husband."

" So be it," said the Tzar's daughter ; and that night, after Finist the Falcon had fallen asleep, she put into his hair the enchanted pin, so that he could not waken, and brought the girl to his room. " Give me, now, the golden hammer and the diamond nails," she said, " and thou mayest keep the flies from him till day-dawn."

So that night too the merchant's daughter leaned over her beloved through the long dark hours, weeping and crying to him : " Finist my love, my bright Falcon, awake and speak to me ! I have come at last to thee ! I have journeyed to the fiftieth Tzardom of the eightieth land, and have washed the blood from thy shirt with my tears !" But because of the enchanted pin Finist could not waken, and at daybreak the girl was sent back to her place in the kitchen.

When Finist came from his chamber, the Tzar's daughter said : " Hast thou slept soundly, and art thou refreshed ?"

He replied : " I slept, but it seemed to me that

one I loved well bent over me, shedding bitter tears and begging me to arise, yet I could not wake. And because of this my own heart is heavy."

And she said: "It was but a dream that to-day's hunting will make thee speedily forget. No one was near thee while thou didst sleep." So Finist the Falcon called for his horse and rode to the open *steppe*.

That day the merchant's daughter wept and was exceeding sorrowful, for on the morrow Finist the Falcon was to be wed. "Never again shall I have the love of my bright falcon," she thought. "Never more, because of my cruel sisters, may I call him to me with the little scarlet flower in my window!" When evening came, however, she dried her tears, sat down for a third time on the soft sand by the blue sea-ocean, and taking out the golden plate, set the diamond ball upon it. That evening also the Tzar's daughter, with her serving-women, came walking on the beach, and as soon as she saw how the little diamond ball was rolling, rolling of itself, she coveted it and said: "Wilt thou sell these also for the same price thou didst ask for thy other playthings?"

" Thou shalt have them," answered the merchant's daughter, "for the same price. Let me only sit through this third night by the side of thy promised husband."

" What a fool is this girl!" thought the Tzar's daughter. " Presently I shall have all her possessions and Finist the Falcon for my husband into the bargain!" So she assented gladly and when Finist the Falcon fell asleep that night, for the third time she put into his hair the enchanted pin and brought the girl into his room, bidding her give over the golden plate and the diamond ball, and keep the flies from him till daybreak.

Through that long night also the merchant's daughter bent over her loved one, weeping and crying : " Finist, my own dear, my bright falcon with coloured feathers, awake and know me ! I have worn through the three pairs of iron shoes, I have broken to pieces the three iron staves, I have gnawed away the three stone church-loaves, all the while searching for thee, my love !" But by reason of the enchanted pin, although he heard through his sleep her crying and lamenting, and his heart grieved because of it, Finist the Falcon could not waken. So at length, when day-dawn was near, the girl said to herself: "Though he shall never be mine, yet in the past he loved me, and for that I shall kiss him once before I go away," and she put her arms about his head to kiss him. As she did so, her hand touched the pin in his hair and she drew it out, lest by chance it harm him. Thus the spell of its enchantment was broken, and one of her tears, falling on his face, woke him.

And instantly, as he awoke, he recognized her, and knew that it was her lamenting he had heard through his sleep. She related to him all that had occurred, how her sisters had plotted, how she had journeyed in search of him, and how she had bought of the Tzar's deceitful daughter the three nights by his side in exchange for the silver spindle, the golden hammer and nails, and the diamond ball that rolled of itself. Hearing, Finist the Falcon was angered against the Tzar's daughter whom he had so nearly wed, but the merchant's daughter he kissed on the mouth, and turning into the falcon, set her on his coloured wings and flew to his own Tzardom.

Then he summoned all his princes and nobles and his officers of all ranks and told them the story, asking: "Which of these two am I to wed? With which can I spend a long life so happily that it will seem a short one : with her who would deceitfully sell my hours for playthings, or with her who sought me over three times nine lands ? Do ye now discuss and decide."

And all cried with one voice : " Thou shouldst leave the seller of thy rest and wed her who did follow thee !"

And so did Finist, the bright falcon with coloured wings.

THE FROG-TZAREVNA

THE FROG-TZAREVNA

In olden time, in a time long before present days, in a certain Tzardom of an Empire far across the blue seas and behind high mountains, there lived a Tzar and his Tzaritza. The Tzar had lived long in the white world, and through long living had become old. He had three sons, Tzareviches, all of them young, brave and unmarried, and altogether of such a sort that they could not be described by words spoken in a tale or written down with a pen. During the long white days they flew about on their fiery, beautiful horses, like bright hawks under the blue sky. All three were handsome and clever, but the handsomest and cleverest was the youngest, and he was Tzarevich Ivan.

One day the Tzar summoned his three sons to his presence and said : " My dear children, ye have now arrived at man's estate and it is time for you to think of marriage. I desire you to select maidens

to be loving wives to you and to me dutiful
daughters-in-law. Take, therefore, your well-arched
bows and arrows which have been hardened in the
fire.   Go into the untrodden field wherein no one
is permitted to hunt, draw the bows tight and shoot
in different directions, and in whatsoever Courts the
arrows fall, there demand your wives-to-be.   She
who brings to each his arrow shall be his bride."

So the Tzareviches made arrows, hardened them
in the fire, and going into the untrodden field, shot
them in different directions.   The eldest brother
shot to the east, the second to the west, and the
youngest, Tzarevich Ivan, drew his bow with all his
strength and shot his arrow straight before him.

On making search, the eldest brother found that
his arrow had fallen in the courtyard of a Boyar,[1]
where it lay before the tower in which were the
apartments of the maidens.   The second brother's
arrow had fallen in the courtyard of a rich merchant
who traded with foreign countries, and pierced a
window at which the merchant's daughter—a lovely
girl soul—was standing.   But the arrow of Tzarevich Ivan could not be found at all.

Tzarevich Ivan searched in deep sorrow and grief.

[1] Nobleman.

For two whole days he wandered in the woods and fields, and on the third day he came by chance to a boggy swamp, where the black soil gave way under the foot, and in the middle of the swamp he came upon a great frog which held in her mouth the arrow he had shot.

When he saw this he turned to run away, leaving his arrow behind him, but the Frog cried: " Kwa ! Kwa ! Tzarevich Ivan, come to me and take thine arrow. If thou wilt not take me for thy wife, thou wilt never get out of this marsh."

Ivan was greatly surprised to hear the frog speak, and was at a loss to know what to do. But at last he took the arrow, picked up the frog, put her in a fold of his coat and went sadly home.

When he arrived at the Palace and told his story, his brothers jeered at him, and the two beautiful maidens whom they were to marry laughed at him also, so that he went weeping to the Tzar and said: " How can I ever take this frog to wife—a little thing that says ' Kwa! Kwa!' She is not my equal. To live one's life long is not like crossing a river or walking over a field. How shall I live with a frog ?"

But the Tzar made answer : " Take her, for such

was my royal word, and such is thy fate!" And
though Tzarevich Ivan wept a long time, there was
no further word to be said, since one cannot go
contrary to his fate.

So the sons of the Tzar were married — the eldest
to the nobleman's daughter, the second to the
daughter of the merchant, and the youngest, Tzarevich Ivan, was married to the frog. When the day
came, he went to the Palace in a closed carriage
and the frog was carried on a golden dish.

So they lived, a long time or a short time, and
Tzarevich Ivan treated the frog with gentleness
and kindness till a day came when the Tzar
summoned his three sons before him and said:
" Dear children, now that ye are wedded, I am
minded to try the skill of my daughters-in-law in
the arts of housewifery. Take from my store-
room, therefore, each of you, a piece of linen cloth,
and his wife shall make of it a shirt which he shall
bring to me to-morrow morning."

The two elder brothers took the linen to their
wives, who at once called together their maid-
servants and nurses and all set to work busily to
cut the stuff and to sew it. And as they worked
they laughed to think of Tzarevich Ivan, saying:

"What will his little Quacker make for him to bring to the Tzar to-morrow?" But Tzarevich Ivan went home looking as if he had swallowed a needle. "How can my little frog-wife make a shirt?" he thought—"she who only creeps on the floor and croaks!" And his bright head hung down lower than his shoulders.

When she saw him, however, the frog spoke. "Kwa! Kwa! Tzarevich Ivan, why art thou so downcast? Hast thou heard from the Tzar thy father a hard, unpleasant word?"

"How can I fail to be downcast?" answered Ivan. "The Tzar, my father, has ordered that thou shouldst sew a shirt out of this linen for him to-morrow."

"Worry not," said the frog, "and have no fear. Go to bed and rest. There is more wisdom in the morning than in the evening!"

When Tzarevich Ivan had laid himself down to sleep, she called servants and bade them cut the linen he had brought into small pieces. Then dismissing them, she took the pieces in her mouth, hopped to the window and threw them out, saying: "Winds! Winds! Fly abroad with these linen shreds and sew me a shirt for the Tzar, my father-

in-law!" And before one could tell it, back into
the room flew a shirt all stitched and finished.

Next morning when Tzarevich Ivan awoke, the
frog presented him with a shirt. "There it is,"
she said. "Take it to thy father and see if it
pleases him." Ivan was greatly rejoiced and
putting the shirt under his coat, set out to the
Palace, where his two elder brothers had already
arrived.

First of all the eldest brother presented his shirt
to his father. The Tzar took it, examined it and
said : "This is sewn in the common way—it is fit
only to be worn in a poor man's hut!" He took
the shirt which the second son had brought, and
said : "This is sewn somewhat better than the
other and is perhaps good enough for me to wear
when I go to my bath." But when he took the shirt
that Tzarevich Ivan presented him, he examined
it with delight, for no single seam could be seen
in it. He could not admire it enough and gave
orders that it should be given him to wear only on
the greatest holidays. Ivan went home happy,
but his two brothers said to one another: "We
need not laugh at Ivan's wife ; she is not really a
frog, but a witch."

A second time the Tzar summoned his three sons and said : " My dear children, I wish to taste bread baked by the hands of my daughters-in-law. Bring me to-morrow morning, therefore, each of you a loaf of soft white bread."

Tzarevich Ivan returned home looking as if he had eaten something without salt, and his bright head hung lower than his shoulders, and when the frog saw him, she said :

" Kwa! Kwa! Kworax! Tzarevich Ivan, why art thou so sad ? Hast thou heard a harsh, un- friendly word from the Tzar thy father ?"

" Why should I not be sad ?" answered Ivan. " The Tzar my father has bidden that thou bake him for to-morrow a loaf of soft white bread."

" Mourn not, Tzarevich Ivan. Be not sad for nothing. Go to bed and sleep in comfort. The morning is wiser than the evening."

When he was asleep she ordered servants to bring a pastry-pot, put flour and cold water into it and make a paste. This she bade them put into the cold oven, and when they were gone she hopped before the oven door and said :

> " Bread, Bread! Be baked !
> Clean, white, and soft as snow !"

Instantly the oven door flew open and the loaf rolled out, cooked crisp and white.

Now the two Tzarevnas, the wives of the other brothers, hated the frog because of the shirt she had made, and when they heard the command of the Tzar, the wife of the eldest brother sent a little black slave-girl to spy on the frog and see what she would do. The black girl hid herself where she could watch, and went and told her mistress what she had seen and heard. Then the two Tzarevnas tried to imitate the frog. They dissolved their flour in cold water, poured the paste into cold ovens and repeated over and over again:

> " Bread, Bread ! Be baked !
> Clean, white, and soft as snow !"

But the ovens remained cold and the paste would not bake.

Seeing this, in anger they gave the poor slave-girl a cruel beating, ordered more flour, made paste with hot water and heated the ovens. But the spilled paste had flowed all about and clogged the flues and made them useless, so that one had her loaf burned on one side and the other took hers out under-baked.

In the morning, when Tzarevich Ivan woke, the
frog sent him to the Palace with his bread wrapped
in a towel, and the brothers came also with theirs.

The Tzar cut the loaf of the eldest son and tasted
it. "Such bread," he said, "might be eaten only
out of misery," and he sent it to the kitchen that it
might be given to the beggars. He tasted that of
the second son and said : "Give this to my
hounds." When Tzarevich Ivan unwrapped his
loaf, however, all exclaimed in admiration. For it
was so splendid that it would be impossible to make
one like it—it could only be told of in tales. It was
adorned with all kinds of cunning designs and on
its sides were wrought the Tzar's cities with their
high walls and gates. The Tzar tasted it and sent
it away, saying: "Put this on my table on Easter
Sunday, when we shall have royal visitors." So
Ivan went home rejoicing.

A third time the Tzar sent for his three sons and
said to them : "My dear children, it is fitting that
all women should know how to weave and broider
in gold and silver, and I would see if thy wives are
skilled also in this. Take, therefore, each of you,
from my storehouse, silk, gold and silver, and to-
morrow morning bring me each of you a carpet."

When Tzarevich Ivan brought sadly home the silk, the gold, and the silver, the frog was sitting on a chair. "Kwa! Kwa! Kworax!" she said. "Tzarevich Ivan, why dost thou mourn? And why doth thy bright head hang down lower than thy shoulders? Hast thou heard from the Tzar thy father a cruel and bitter word?"

"Have I not cause to mourn?" he answered. "The shirt thou hast sewn, and the bread thou has baked; but now my father has bidden that thou make for to-morrow a carpet of this gold, silver, and silk."

"Fret not, Tzarevich Ivan," said the frog. "Lay thee down and rest. The day has more wisdom than the night."

As soon as he was asleep she called servants and bade them take scissors and cut to pieces all the silk, the gold, and the silver, and then, sending them away, threw it out of the window, and said:

"Winds! Winds! fly abroad with these pieces of silk, of gold, and of silver, and make me a carpet such as my dear father used to cover his windows!" And hardly had she said the last word, when back into the room flew the embroidered carpet.

Now again the wives of the elder brothers had

sent the little black slave-girl to watch, and she ran quickly to tell them. And they, thinking that this time the charm must work, cut all of their silk and precious thread into pieces, threw them out of the window, and repeated :

" Winds ! Winds ! fly abroad with these pieces of silk, of gold, and of silver, and make us carpets such as our dear fathers used to cover their windows."

But though they waited a long time, the winds brought them no carpets. Then the Tzarevnas, angry at the loss of their rich threads, after beating the little slave-girl more cruelly than before, sent servants hastily for more material, and calling together their nurses and maidens to help them, began to work at weaving and embroidering.

In the morning when Tzarevich Ivan arose, the frog sent him to the Palace to show his carpet with his brothers.

The Tzar looked at the carpet of the eldest son and said : " Take this to the stables. It will do to cover my poorest horse when it is raining." He looked at the carpet of the second, and said : " Put this in the hall ; it may do, perhaps, to wipe my boots upon in bad weather." But when Tzarevich

Ivan unrolled his carpet, so wondrously was it
adorned with gold and silver fashionings, that its
like cannot be imagined. And the Tzar ordered
that it be kept with the greatest care, to be put on
his own table on the most solemn feast-days.

"Now, my dear children," he said, "your wives,
my daughters-in-law, have done all that I bade
them do. Bring them to-morrow, therefore, to
the Palace to dine, in order that I may con-
gratulate them in person."

The two elder brothers went home to their wives,
saying to one another: "Now he must bring his
frog-wife with him to the royal audience for all
to see!" But Tzarevich Ivan went home weeping,
and his bright head hung down lower than his
shoulders.

When he reached home the frog was sitting at
the door. "Kwa! Kwa! Kworax!" she said.
"Tzarevich Ivan, why dost thou weep? Hast
thou heard sharp and unfeeling words from the
Tzar thy father?"

"Why should I not weep?" he answered. "Thou
hast sewn the shirt, thou hast baked the bread, and
thou hast woven the carpet; but after all thou art
but a frog, and to-morrow the Tzar my father

commands that I bring thee to the Palace to royal audience. How, to my shame, can I show thee to the people as my wife?"

"Weep no more," the frog said. "Go to thy bed and sleep. There is more wisdom in the morning than in the evening."

The next day when Tzarevich Ivan awoke, she said: "Pay no heed to what others think. The Tzar thy father was pleased with his shirt, his bread and his carpet; maybe he will be pleased also with his daughter-in-law when I shall come. Do thou go to the Palace and I will come after thee in an hour. Make thy respects to the Tzar, and when thou hearest a rumbling and a knocking, say: 'Hither comes my poor little frog in her little basket!'"

So Ivan drove away to the Palace somewhat cheered by her words.

When he was out of sight the frog went to the window, and called:

"Winds! Winds! bring for me at once a rich carriage of state, with white horses, footmen, outriders and runners!"

Instantly a horn blew and horsemen came galloping up the street, followed by six milk-white horses drawing a golden coach. As for herself, she threw off the skin of a frog and was transformed into a maiden so beautiful that she could be described neither by words in a tale nor with a pen in writing.

Meanwhile at the Palace the company were assembled, the two elder brothers with their lovely brides attired in silks and laden with shining jewels. And they all laughed at Tzarevich Ivan standing alone, saying: "Where is thy wife, the Tzarevna? Why didst thou not bring her in a kitchen cloth? And art thou certain that thou didst choose the greatest beauty of the swamp?" But while they jeered at poor Ivan, suddenly there came a great rumbling and shouting. The Tzar supposed some King or Prince was arriving to visit him, but Tzarevich Ivan said: "Be not disturbed, little father. It is only my poor little frog coming in her little basket."

Nevertheless everybody ran to the Palace windows, and they saw riders galloping and a golden coach drawn by six milk-white horses flew up to the entrance and out of it came the lovely maiden —such a beauty as to make the sun and moon ashamed when she looked at them. She came to Tzarevich Ivan and he took her hand and led her to the Tzar his father and the Tzar himself seated her at the royal table to dine.

As all began to feast and make merry, the wives of the elder sons whispered among themselves and said : " It is as we have thought. She is in truth a witch. Let us watch carefully and whatever she does let us be careful to do likewise. So, watching, they saw that the frog-wife did not drink the dregs of her wine-cup, but poured them in her left sleeve, and that the bones of the roast swan she put in her right sleeve, and they did the same.

When they rose from the table, the musicians began to play and the Tzar led out Ivan's beautiful wife to dance. This she did with exceeding grace. And as she danced she waved her left sleeve, and at one end of the banquet hall a lake appeared one rod deep. She waved her right sleeve and swans and geese appeared swimming on it. The Tzar and his guests were astonished and could not sufficiently praise her cleverness. When she finished dancing the lake and the fowls upon it disappeared.

Then the wives of the elder sons began to dance. They waved their left sleeves and all the guests were splashed with the wine dregs ; they waved their right sleeves and the bones flew right and

left, and one nearly put out one of the Tzar's eyes.
At this he was angered, and straightway ordered
them out of the Palace, so that they went home in
shame and dishonour.

Now seeing what a beautiful creature his little
frog-wife had become, Tzarevich Ivan thought to
himself: "What if she should turn back into a frog
again !" And while they were dancing he hastened
home, searched till he found the frog-skin and
threw it into the fire.

His wife, arriving, ran to search for the skin and
when she could not find it, guessed what he had
done.

She immediately fell aweeping and said : " Alas,
alas, Tzarevich Ivan, that thou couldst not have
patience even for a little while ! Now thou hast
lost me for ever, unless thou canst find me beyond
three times nine lands, in the thirtieth Tzardom, in
the empire that lies under the sun. Know that I
am the fairy Wassilissa the Wise." When she had
said this she turned into a blue dove and flew out
of the window.

Tzarevich Ivan wept till his tears were like a
river, then he said a prayer to God and bidding the
Tzar his father and the Tzaritza his mother fare-

well, went whither his eyes looked, in search of his
lost wife.

He went on and on; whether it was near or far,
or a short road or a long road, a tale is soon told,
but such a journey is not made quickly. He
travelled through thrice nine lands, asking everyone
he met where he could find Wassilissa the Wise,
but none could answer, till he reached the empire
that lies under the sun, and there in the thirtieth
Tzardom he met an old grey-beard to whom he
told his story and asked his question.

" Well do I know of Wassilissa the Wise,"
answered the old man. " She is a powerful fairy
whose father, in a fit of anger, turned her into a
frog for three years. The time was almost up, and
hadst thou not burned her frog-skin she would be
with thee now. I cannot tell thee where she is,
but take thou this magic ball which will roll
wherever thou commandest it, and follow it."

Tzarevich Ivan thanked the old grey-beard,
threw the ball he gave him on the ground and
at his command it straightway began to roll. It
rolled a short way and it rolled a long way, it rolled
across a pebbly plain and into a drear and dreadful
forest, and in the middle of the forest he came to a

miserable little hut that stood on hens' legs and
turned continually round and round.   And Ivan
said to it :

> " Little hut ! little hut !
> Stand the way thy mother placed thee,
> With thy back to the wood and thy front to me !"

And immediately the hut turned about facing
him and stood still.

Tzarevich Ivan climbed up one of its hens' legs
and entered the door, and there he saw the oldest
of the Baba-Yagas, the bony-legged grandmother
of all the witches, lying on a corner of the stove
on· nine bricks, with one lip on the shelf, her nose
(which was as long as the Perevitzky Bridge) thrust
up the chimney, and her huge iron mortar in
the corner.

"Poo !" she cried, gnashing her teeth, "who is
this comes to me ?   Until now I have neither seen
with my eyes nor heard with my ears the spirit of
any Russian ; but to-day it is a Russian who enters
my house !   Well, Tzarevich Ivan, camest thou
hither from thine own wish, or because thou wast
compelled ?"

" Enough by my own will and twice as much by
force," answered Tzarevich Ivan.   " But for shame,

thou, that thou hast not offered me to eat and to drink, and prepared me a bath !"

Then the Baba-Yaga, being pleased with his spirit, gave him food and drink and made ready a bath for him ; and when he had refreshed himself, he related to her the whole affair just as it had been. And when she learned that Wassilissa the Wise was in truth his wife, she said : " I will indeed render thee this service, not for love of thee, but because I hate her father. The fairy flies across this forest every day, bringing messages for her father, and stops in my house to rest. Remain here, and as soon as she enters, seize her by the head. When she feels herself caught, she will turn into a frog, and from a frog to a lizard, and from a lizard to a snake, and last of all she will transform herself into an arrow. Do thou take the arrow and break it into three pieces, and she will be thine for ever ! But take heed when thou hast hold of her not to let her go."

The Baba-Yaga concealed the Tzarevich behind the stove and scarcely was he hidden when in flew Wassilissa the Wise. Ivan crept up noiselessly behind her and seized her by the head. She instantly turned into a great green frog and he laughed with joy to see her in the form he knew so well. When she turned into a lizard, however, the cold touch of the creature was so loathsome that he let go his hold, and immediately the lizard darted through a crack in the floor.

The Baba-Yaga upbraided him. "How shouldst thou win back such a wife," she said, "thou who canst not touch the skin of a creeping lizard? As thou couldst not keep her, thou shalt never again see her here. But if thou likest, go to my sister and see if she will help thee."

Tzarevich Ivan did so. The ball rolled a long way and it rolled a short way, across a mountain and into a deep ravine, and here he came to a second wretched little hovel turning round on hens' legs. He made it stand still and entered it as before, and there on the stove, with one lip on the shelf and her nose propping the ceiling, was the skinny grand-aunt of all the witches.

To her he told his story, and for the sake of her sister the Baba-Yaga also agreed to help him. "Wassilissa the Wise," she said, "rests in my house too, but if this time thou lettest go thy hold, thou mayest never clasp her more." So she hid Tzarevich Ivan and when Wassilissa came

flying in, he sprang upon her and seized her and
did not flinch even when she turned into a lizard in
his hands. But when he beheld the lizard change
to a fierce and deadly snake, he cried out in alarm
and loosed his hold, and the snake wriggled through
the doorway and disappeared.

Then was Tzarevich Ivan exceeding sorrowful,
so that he did not even hear the reproaches of
the old witch. So bitterly did he weep that she
pitied him and said : "Little enough dost thou
deserve this wife of thine, but if thou choosest, go
to my younger sister and see if she will help thee.
For Wassilissa the Wise stops to rest also at her
house. So, plucking up heart somewhat, Tzarevich
Ivan obeyed.

The ball rolled a long way and it rolled a short
way ; it crossed a broad river, and there on the
shore he came to a third hut, wretcheder than
the other two put together, turning round on hens'
legs, and in it was the second grand-aunt of all
the witches. She too consented to aid him. "But
remember," she said, "if this time thy heart
fails and thy hand falters, never again shalt thou
behold thy wife in the white world !"

So a third time Tzarevich Ivan hid himself, and

presently in came flying Wassilissa the Wise, and this time he said a prayer to God as he sprang out and seized her in a strong grasp. In vain she turned into a frog, into a cold lizard and into a deadly, writhing snake. Ivan's grip did not loosen. At last she turned into an arrow and this he immediately snatched and broke into three pieces. At the same moment the lovely Wassilissa, in her true maiden shape, appeared and threw herself into his arms. "Now, Tzarevich Ivan," she said, "I give myself up to thy will!"

The Baba-Yaga gave them for a present a white mare which could fly like the wind, and on the fourth day it set them down safe and sound at the Tzar's Palace.

He received them with joy and thankfulness, and made a great feast, and after that he made Tzarevich Ivan Tzar in his stead.

SCHMAT-RAZUM

SCHMAT-RAZUM

Before our grandfathers had learned anything, before their grandfathers were born, there was, in the Court of the Tzar of a far Tzardom, a young bowman named Taraban who was the cleverest of all the royal archers. Each day he went hunting in the fens and marshes for wild swans for the Palace table, and one evening, as he wandered with his bow and arrows, he saw seven white ducks with silver wings resting beneath a tree. So beautiful were they that he would not shoot them, but when they flew away followed them afoot, thinking: "Perhaps when they alight again I may catch one alive." The ducks alighted on the shore of the sea-ocean and there they laid aside their silver wings and becoming transformed into lovely maidens, threw themselves into the water and began to bathe.

The archer crept noiselessly near and without

being seen, took the silver wings of the one he thought the most beautiful, and hid himself.

Presently the damsels finished their bathing and coming from the water, ran to put on their silver wings, and behold one pair was missing. Then she who owned them called to the others and said: "Fly abroad, my little sisters! Fly abroad and linger not for me! I must stay and search for my wings. If I find them I will overtake you, but if not, when our mother asks of me, tell her I remained to listen to the song of the nightingale."

The six maidens thereupon put on their silver wings and turning again to white ducks, flew away over the sea-ocean, while the one who remained began to weep. Weeping, she cried: "Show thyself, I pray, thou who hast evilly taken my silver wings. If thou art a girl, I will be to thee a sister. If warrior or lady, I will be thy daughter. And if a youth, I will be thy wife. Only give me back my silver wings!"

When Taraban heard her words he was filled with pity, and showing himself at once, gave her the wings. "I would not cause thee grief or sorrow, damsel," he said. "Take them and be free

for all of me. And for thy tears I ask thy forgiveness."

Then the maiden looked on him wonderingly and
said : " Right kindly dost thou speak, though I
have been taught that men were hard and cruel.
Nevertheless a word given cannot be recalled and
if thou art so minded, I will wed thee. Perhaps I
shall not repent."

The archer rejoiced and kissed and caressed her,
and they lay down, each under a little shrub, and
slept till daybreak, when he took her to the capital
and they were married. Then Taraban bethought
himself of his duty, and leaving her at home, went
to the Palace and prostrated himself before the Tzar.

" Health to thee, my best bowman !" said the
Tzar. " What wouldst thou ask ?"

" O Tzar's Majesty !" he said, " I am guilty
before thee ! I have wedded a wife without thy
royal permission."

" Well," said the Tzar, " thy fault is not a great
one. Come hither to-morrow, however, and bring
thy wife that she may salute me. Then I may
know whether she whom thou hast chosen will
ornament my Court."

So, next day, Taraban brought his wife to the

Palace, and her beauty was such that it made the other ladies of the Court look like crows. The Tzar could not gaze sufficiently at her and the instant she had gone felt himself seized with a violent love for her. He sent in hot haste for his Court Ministers, his Boyars, and his great Generals, and said: " Here are the keys of my royal treasury. Take as much gold as ye require to search throughout the four corners of the white world. Only fetch me, to become my Tzaritza, such another beauty as the wife of my archer !"

They answered: "O Tzar's Majesty! we are already in the latter half of our lives and never have we seen one to be compared with her !" The Tzar, however, headstrong and evil-tempered, would not listen, and bidding them go at once and begin the search, sent them from his presence in displeasure.

The Boyars and Councillors scratched their grey heads and stroked their beards. They were so depressed that their very noses drooped, but they had, perforce, to go upon the highway to search. While they were thus engaged a ragged beggar approached them. " Why are ye so cast down, O Boyars and gentlemen ?" he asked.

"Get thee gone, thou bundle of rags!" they said.

"Best not to drive me away," the beggar replied. "Rather give me a piece of gold, and I will point you out the road of cleverness."

Thereupon one of them gave him the piece of gold, when he crossed himself and said : "O Boyars and gentlemen, well do I know thy quest. However, another maiden as lovely as the wife of Taraban the archer ye will not find in the whole world. Sooner will beards grow from the palms of your hands. It is of no use to search for her and as the Tzar will be satisfied with nothing less, your heads will pay for your failure. Go ye back therefore to the Tzar and bid him command the archer to journey across three times nine lands to the little forest monster Muzhichek, who is as high as the knee, with mustaches seven *versts* long, and to bring hither his invisible servant, Schmat-Razum, who lives in his master's pocket and doth all that he orders him. Bid the Tzar demand this of the archer, and he shall have his will. For while Muzhichek indeed exists, no man can find his dwelling nor perceive his invisible servant, and Taraban will wander all his life long, though he live for

ever, without accomplishing the task, and the Tzar
may have his beautiful wife."

The Boyars and Ministers were rejoiced. They
loaded the beggar with gold and returning to the
Palace, advised the Tzar to act upon this counsel,
and he, being cruel and wicked of heart, did so.
He summoned the archer and said:

"Taraban, my well-loved bowman, and best of
my archers! On account of thy loyalty, I have
chosen thee out for an especial service. Across
three times nine lands dwells the forest monster
Muzhichek, who is as high as the knee, with
mustaches seven *versts* long. Bring to me his
servant Schmat-Razum, who lives in his pocket,
and thou shalt be chiefest of all my Boyars. But
as thou lovest thy life, mind thou return not without him!"

The archer went home in great distress and his
wife, noticing his sorrowful look, asked: "What
has saddened thee? Hast thou had an unfriendly
word from the Tzar? Or perchance do I no
longer please thy fancy?"

"Thou pleasest me but too well, my dearest
wife," he answered, "but thy beauty now has
brought ruin upon me!" And he began to weep.

She besought him to tell what had befallen, and when he had told her, she said : " The Tzar is indeed thy prime enemy and hath set thee a grievous task, and there is no one in the white world who can aid thee unless it be my little mother. I will send thee to her for advice. Go first to the Tzar and ask for a purse of money sufficient for a year and come back to me."

Taraban did so, and returned with the purse to his wife, when she gave him a crystal ball and a silken handkerchief. " After thou art well out of the city," she said, " throw this ball upon the ground, and follow whither it rolls. It will lead thee to my little mother. As for the handkerchief, as often as thou dost wash, dry thy face upon it and upon no other."

So the archer bade her farewell and set out. He threw down the ball, which rolled always before him, and it led him across three times nine countries till he had journeyed for the space of a whole year.

Now when he had been absent three months, the Tzar called his Ministers and said : " The archer has been gone a fourth part of a year, and no doubt he will never return. I see not why I should wait longer. Go ye, therefore, and bring his wife to the

Palace." They went, accordingly, and brought her to him and he straightway began to speak endearing words to her; but she repulsed him and cried out upon him, saying: "Though thou art a great Tzar, yet I am a wife and Taraban thy archer is my husband, and I will have no other!"

"If thou wilt not love me willingly, then will I compel thee!" swore the Tzar, and bade them build a square tower beside the blue sea-ocean, and shutting her within it, locked its door with seven locks and surrounded it with soldiers and with ships till she should look kindly upon him. So she abode alone in the square tower, watching always for the return of her husband.

As for the archer, when he had journeyed a year, following the crystal ball, he reached at length an empty land which had no trace of a human footstep, where was naught for eye to see or ear to hear, and crossing this he came to the sea-ocean, where, white and dazzling on the beach, stood a vast and splendid Palace to whose gate the ball led him. He entered and there met him six lovely damsels, who greeted him kindly and seeing that he was travel-worn and wearied, gave him food and drink and made him lie down and rest.

BADE THEM BUILD A SQUARE TOWER . . . . AND SHUTTING HER WITHIN IT . . . . SURROUNDED
IT WITH SOLDIERS AND WITH SHIPS.

When he rose they brought him a golden wash-basin and an embroidered towel, but the towel he would not use, drying his face on the handkerchief he carried with him. No sooner did he show this, however, than they looked at it and cried: "This handkerchief we know! Where didst thou obtain it?"

"It was given me by my wife," he replied.

"Then thou hast wedded our little sister!" they exclaimed, and led him to their mother, where she sat in a silver chair. To her he recounted how he had won his wife and how they had lived happily together till the Tzar had sent him on his present quest, and how she had given him the crystal ball that had brought him thither.

The old mother said: "My dear son-in-law, I have lived nine-tenths of my life on this earth, and I indeed know of Muzhichek, the forest monster, but where he lives I cannot tell, and never have I heard of his servant Schmat-Razum. Perhaps, however, I may discover for thee where he may be found." Then going to a balcony which overlooked the land, she cried with a piping voice: "Harken, all ye fowls and flying things, ye bees and insects! Come to me!" And immediately there came

flying to her from every side all manner of birds
and insects till the sky was dark with them. Then
she cried : "O ye, my friends, who fly everywhere
in all four directions, have ye by chance heard tell
of Schmat-Razum?" And the birds and insects
answered with one voice : "No, we have not heard
of him."

She dismissed them to their bowers and coverts,
and going to a balcony which overlooked the sea-
ocean, she cried : " Hearken, all ye fish and swimming things! Come to me!" And straightway
there came swimming toward the shore, from every
part of the water, all the fish of the sea-ocean, till
the blue waves were not to be seen for the number
of them. Then she cried : " O ye, my friends, who
swim everywhere in all waters salt and fresh, have
ye perchance heard of Schmat-Razum?" And they
replied, all together: " No, we know nothing of
him."

She bade them go back to their deep sea-caves,
and descending to the garden, cried : " Harken, all
ye beasts and creeping things! Come hither!"
And at once there came hastening from all sides
every kind of beast and reptile till the ground was
black with them. "O ye, my friends, who run and

creep everywhere in all lands," she cried, "have ye ever heard of Schmat-Razum?" And all answered in one voice: "No, we have never heard of him."

She sent them away to their jungles and thickets, when an aged frog, who from lameness had arrived behind the others, hopped forward and said: "I have heard of Schmat-Razum, the servant of Muzhichek, the forest monster. His master lives on a mountain in a forest in the Tzardom of Tzar Zmey, and the forest I know well. But it is at the very end of the world and I cannot travel so far in less than fifty years."

The old mother bade her daughters fetch a jar of milk and put into it the frog and gave it to the archer. "Take this with thee," she said, "and the frog will show thee the road." So Taraban took the jar and bidding the old mother and her six daughters farewell, set out.

Whether the way was short or long, or its end far or near, he came at length to the Tzardom of Tzar Zmey, to where was a high mountain covered with a forest. He ascended the mountain, and at its very top was an iron door. "Now, good youth," said the frog, "this door is the entrance to the cavern which is the abode of Muzhichek. As to

Schmat-Razum, his servant, go with God, for I cannot aid thee!"

The archer thanked the frog, set the jar on the soft moss, and opening the iron door, entered the cavern. Within it was dark enough to put one's eyes out. Groping about, he found under a table an empty chest in which he hid himself and waited to see what would happen.

He lay there one hour, he waited another and a third, when suddenly there came a rumbling from without, the door was nearly torn from its hinges, and in came the forest monster. He was as high as a knee, had swine's bristles for hair, and his mustaches, seven *versts* long, floated far out of the cavern behind him.

Muzhichek sat himself down at the table and thundered: " Ho! Schmat-Razum! Out of my pocket and fetch me my supper!" Instantly lamps lit themselves on the walls, plates laid themselves on the table covered with cooked flesh and fowl of every description, and bottles of wine appeared and poured their contents into goblets. The forest monster ate and drank to surfeit, making a noise like a mill, till there was nothing left. Then he shouted: "Ho! Schmat-Razum! Clear my table!"

And immediately the empty plates and goblets disappeared and the lamps on the walls went out. Muzhichek then bade him remain and keep his house for him till his return, and rushed away down the mountain.

The archer crept out of the chest then, and seating himself at the table, shouted : " Ho ! Schmat-Razum ! Bring me food and drink !" At once the lamps reappeared and the table was spread as before. Then he said : " Ho ! Schmat-Razum ! Thou shouldst be hungry too. Sit thee down and eat and drink with me for company's sake."

Then, though Taraban saw no one, a voice answered him and said : " Whence comest thou, good youth ? For three times nine years have I served my master here and never has he asked me, as dost thou, to sup with him !"

" Nevertheless, Schmat-Razum," said the archer, " sit thee down. Perhaps I like thy company better than doth thy master." He began to eat and drink and opposite him the plates and wine-glasses emptied themselves, so that he knew the invisible servant was also eating and drinking. When the meal was finished the archer said : " Ho ! Schmat-Razum ! it seems to me thy master, the forest monster, doth not use thee too well. Wilt thou be my servant, instead ? I will not use thee worse."

" Why not ?" answered the other. " I am right tired of this cavern. I see thou art a good companion besides."

" Come with me at once, then," said the archer, " for my home is far away."

He left the cavern, picked up the jar with the frog and shouted for his servant. " Here I am, master," said a voice at his elbow. " Thou canst not see me, yet I shall be ever by thee to execute thy commands."

Taraban set out and made such good speed that even had Muzhichek known what direction his servant had taken, he would have had trouble enough to overtake him. They came to the deserted land where stood the splendid Palace, and rested there three weeks, and Schmat-Razum feasted the archer and his mother-in-law and her six daughters every day. Taraban left there the aged frog, whom the old mother promised, for her services, three jars of fresh milk every nine days for ever. Then, with his invisible servant, Taraban set out again for his own Tzardom.

He journeyed six months without stopping and

at the end of that time was so wearied that he
could scarce set one foot before the other, and
at length he sank down on the ground, saying:
"Schmat-Razum, my faithful servant! Thou must
find another master, for I am utterly exhausted
and I fear me I shall never see my own Tzardom
and my dear wife again!"

"Why didst thou not tell me thou wast
wearied?" said Schmat-Razum; "I will carry
thee as far and as swiftly as thou desirest!" And
instantly Taraban felt himself lifted as if by a
whirlwind, and borne through the air with such
exceeding swiftness that he could scarce see the
rivers and forests, the towns and villages, flying
past. Presently he perceived far beneath him the
waves of the blue sea-ocean and there their pace
slackened and Schmat-Razum said: "Master, wilt
thou not bid me here make thee a resting-place?"

"Do so," said Taraban; and at once there was
a mighty whirlpool in the sea below and a green
island appeared clothed with a pleasant wood. At
its edge was a garden full of flowers of seven
colours and glowing shrubbery, and in the garden
was a golden summer-house, with silken awnings
of many hues, and windows looking out over the

sea-ocean.   They descended and Schmat-Razum
said : " Rest here, master, I pray thee, and refresh
thyself for some days and then we will resume our
journey."

So there they rested.   Next day a merchant
vessel came sailing by and the ship's master saw
the island and put in near shore and cast anchor.
Taraban welcomed him, took him into his golden
summer - house and brought him a stool to sit
upon.   " Abide here," he said, " and divert thyself
with me for a season, for there is no one with me
save my servant here."

The shipman said : " But I see no servant."

" Thou shalt presently understand," said the
archer, and called : " Ho ! Schmat-Razum ! bring
hither wine and savoury meats !" and immediately
a table was spread with all kinds of delicacies.
The master of the ship was much astonished and
admired greatly the invisible servant, and for the
space of a whole day besought the archer to sell
him, offering for him a great store of gold.   When
Taraban would not, he fetched from his ship a
little crystal casket.   He raised its lid and immediately the wind began to blow and the waves rose,
till the level of the water was ten feet higher than

before ; he closed the lid, and the waves grew still
and the water subsided. In addition to his gold,
the ship's master offered this casket in exchange
for Schmat-Razum, but the archer would not.

The next day a second ship came sailing across
the sea-ocean and stopped at the island. It carried
a rich merchant, who had himself rowed ashore in
a skiff and, like the first, was welcomed by Taraban.
He too desired the invisible servant, and for two
days tried to persuade the archer to sell him. He
offered for him a heap of precious stones without
number and at length, returning to his ship,
brought an earthen bowl which he offered in
exchange. He tapped the bowl's side and it
produced a full rigged ship-of-war with all its
sailors and fighting men. He tapped fifty times
and with each tap it brought forth a like ship, with
sails spread and mariners and soldiers in their
places, till a fleet of fifty lay off the island. Then
he turned the bowl upside down and ships and
men at once disappeared. But the archer would
not exchange Schmat-Razum for the magic bowl.

While both ships lay at anchor there came a
third vessel, bearing a trader from a distant Tzardom, and he too came to rest on the island. So

much did he desire to possess the archer's servant
that after he had bargained for the space of three
days, he offered Taraban the value of his whole
ship's cargo ; and when that did not suffice, he
drew from his pocket a golden horn which he
offered in addition. He blew into one end of it
and instantly a great host appeared, both horsemen
and footmen, with spears and armour shining like
gold. The officers of the host waved their bright
swords and the musicians played warlike music,
and the foot soldiers marched and the troopers
galloped past; then the tradesman blew into its
other end and all in an instant vanished. But
neither for the wonderful horn would Taraban
give up his servant Schmat-Razum.

Now the three vessels prepared to put out to sea,
and presently Schmat-Razum came to the archer,
and said : " Master, thy three guests, the captain,
the merchant and the tradesman, purpose to
do thee ill. I but now heard them plotting
together how they may slay thee, because thou
wilt not trade me to them. Now exchange me, I
pray thee, for the casket, the bowl and the horn,
and let them take me away. For at any moment
thou desirest me I will return."

Accordingly Taraban went to the three men and said: "Thy wonders seemed to me to be less than mine, but it has occurred to me that with fleets and hosts I can take high service under some Tzar, and fighting is my trade. So if ye will agree to give me your three wonders in exchange for him, ye may have my servant."

The three conferred together. "It is much," they said; "but after all, we are merchantmen, and of what use to us are high tides, hosts and ships of war? With Schmat-Razum, however, we may live together in plenty all our lives and have whatever our hearts desire." So they gave the archer the casket, the bowl and the horn, and he bade Schmat-Razum go with them, and they boarded one of their vessels and sailed away in company across the blue sea-ocean.

For three little days they regaled their crews and themselves feasted royally, drinking their fill each night and sleeping heavily, while the archer sat alone in the golden summer-house on the island. On the fourth evening, Taraban, finding loneliness sit heavily upon him, sighed and said to himself: "Oh, Schmat-Razum, my faithful servant! How long will it be before I hear thy voice again?"

And at that moment Schmat-Razum replied at his elbow, "Here I am, master; I but waited thy call."

The archer rejoiced. "It is time for us to go to my own Tzardom," he said. And in a twinkling, island and summer-house vanished and the whirlwind lifted him and bore him away.

Next morning the captain, the merchant and the trader awoke on the vessel. "Ho! Schmat-Razum!" they cried, "bring us a cooling drink!" But there was no answer and the service was not rendered. They ran hither and thither and shouted and bawled, but the invisible servant was gone. In anger they put about and returned to the place where the archer's island had been, but no trace of it could they find. Then they said to one another: "This was a magician, and he has cheated and fooled us! May the devil take him!" And weeping and lamenting, they spread their sails and departed, each in a different direction.

Meanwhile the archer was carried by the whirlwind across the sea-ocean to his own Tzardom, and there on the shore he perceived the square tower which the Tzar had built, surrounded by its ships and soldiers. "Leave me here, Schmat-Razum," he said, "and go and see who is guarded in that tower."

He felt himself set gently on the sea-beach, and presently Schmat-Razum returned and said: "Master, some beauteous princess sits in the tower's upper chamber, bemoaning the absence of her husband whom the Tzar has sent across three times nine lands, because he desires to possess her himself."

"It is doubtless my own lovely wife!" the archer exclaimed, and sent his servant to her with a message bidding her be of good cheer. Then he ordered Schmat-Razum to take him to the Tzar's Palace, and at once was set down under the royal windows. There he lifted his voice and cried: "O thou wicked Tzar! Thou stealer of thy subjects' wives! Come thou out to me that I, thy archer, may tell thee to thy face what thou art!"

The captain of the Palace Guard, hearing, thought him mad and sent a soldier to seize him, but the soldier Schmat-Razum overthrew in an instant. The captain sent a squad and them also he stretched on the ground like sheaves of barley, while the archer did not so much as lift a hand, but continued to shout against the Tzar.

Hearing the uproar, the Tzar himself at length came to the window and seeing the archer and hearing his words, waxed exceeding wroth. " Wilt thou suffer this insolent bowman," he cried, " to revile me before my own Palace ?" And he sent in haste for his soldiers. They assembled, but as they came, the archer took his golden horn and blew it and at once the invincible host appeared, horse and foot, glittering in bright armour. He began to rap on his earthen bowl and instantly ships-of-war were along all the coast. He opened his crystal casket and the waves rose and the water lifted ten feet, so that the ships came sailing up to the very walls of the capital.

The watchmen sitting on the Tzar's watch-towers cried to those beneath that a hundred war-ships had arrived under sail and were coming to attack the capital, and they hastened to tell the Tzar. Furious, he mounted his horse and rode out at the head of all his army and bade them open battle.

Taraban called the captains of his host and gave them orders. The musicians began to play and the horses to chafe and fume, the drummers beat their drums, and the horsemen and footmen moved

forward like a great river. Nothing could stop
them. The enchanted swords cut down the Tzar's
men like grain and the gleaming spears pierced
through their armour, so that soon all his army
was in flight. The Tzar himself was caught
between the two forces, dashed from his horse
and trampled to death in an instant.

Then the archer called together his host, while
the Ministers and Boyars, terror-stricken, besought
him to spare their lives and rule the Tzardom.
He consented and marching to the tower, brought
his wife in all honour to the Palace, where, when all
had kissed her hand as their Tzaritza, he ordered a
great festival. For three weeks the whole realm
feasted till the royal bins were empty and the
cellars ran dry, while the host encamped round
about the capital and the ships of war flocked under
its walls.

On the twenty-first night, at midnight, Taraban
went to his chamber, turned upside-down the
earthen bowl, blew into the golden horn and closed
the casket, and at the same moment the sea receded,
the great host and the fleet of warships vanished,
and all was as before.

So Taraban the archer began his reign, and his

rule was wise and terrible. He subdued other Tzardoms and begat many children and lived in joy all the days of his life, with his Tzaritza and his faithful servant, Schmat-Razum.

LITTLE BEAR'S-SON

LITTLE BEAR'S-SON.

In a certain Tzardom of the thirtieth realm, across three times nine lands, beyond the sea-ocean, there once lived an old peasant with his wife. They were honest and industrious, though they did not swim in cheese and butter. Indeed, they were very poor and moreover had no children, which was a great grief to them. In scanty seasons the peasant eked out his living by hunting wolves and bears, whose skins he marketed to buy bread.

One day he tracked a bear to its den and having killed it, he found there to his astonishment a little boy three years old, naked and sturdy, whom the bear had stolen and had been rearing like a cub. The peasant took the little boy home, called in the priest, had him baptized Ivashko Medvedko, which is to say "Little Ivan, Bear's-Son," and began to bring him up as his own.

The lad grew not by years, but by hours, as fast

as if someone were dragging him upstairs, until
when he was fifteen he was of a man's height and
stronger than anyone in the whole countryside.
He did not realize his own strength, so that before
long, as he played with the other lads of the village,
accidents began to happen. When he would seize
a playmate by the hand it was a piece of luck if
he did not pull the hand off, and arms and even
heads were separated from their bodies when he
was made angry.

This naturally produced much trouble, and
finally his neighbours came to the old peasant and
said : " Thou art our neighbour and our country-
man and we have no quarrel with thee. But as for
thy ' bear's-son,' he should be thrust forth from the
village. We do not choose longer to have our little
children maimed by his antics."

The old man was sad and sorry, for he loved the
lad and knew that he was of a good heart and
meant no mischief. Little Bear's-Son noticed his
downcast looks and asked : " Why art thou so sad,
little grandfather ? Who has taken away thy
happiness ?"

" Ah, little grandson," said the old man, sighing
heavily, " thou hast been my only comfort. Now

our neighbours have determined to expell thee from the village, and what wilt thou do, and how wilt thou live ?"

"Well, little grandfather," answered he, "this is truly a great misfortune, but it cannot be helped. Go thou, I pray, and buy me an iron club of twenty-five *poods* weight. Let me remain here but three weeks longer, to exercise and develop my body, and then I shall leave thee to make mine own way in the white world, to show myself and to be seen." The old man went and bought the heavy iron club, loaded it in a cart and brought it home, and with it Little Bear's-Son began each day to exercise.

Now near by was a green meadow on which stood three fir-trees ; the first was fifteen reaches around, the second twenty, and the third twenty-five. When the first week was ended he went to the meadow, seized the first fir-tree and putting forth all his strength, pulled it over. He went home and exercised with his iron club a second week, and at the end of that time he went to the meadow, seized the second fir-tree, bent it down to the ground and broke it into two pieces. He went home and exercised with his iron club yet a third week, and going to the meadow, he seized the third fir-tree and with a single jerk tore it up by the roots. So mighty was his strength that the earth shook, the forest moaned, the sea-ocean began to boil and the fir - tree was reduced to powder. "Now," said Little Bear's-Son, "I am so strong that I fear not even a witch," and bidding farewell, with tears, to the old man and the old woman, he thrust his iron club into his girdle and went whither his eyes looked.

Whether he wandered a long way or a short way, he came at length to a river three *versts* wide. On its bank knelt a giant, as tall as a birch sapling, and as thick as a hayrick, with his mouth stretched wide in the water, catching fish with his mustache. When he caught one, he kindled a fire on his tongue, roasted and swallowed it.

" Health to thee, giant," said Little Bear's-Son. " Who art thou ?"

" Health to thee," answered the other. " My name is Usynia.[1] Whither goest thou ?"

" Whither my eyes look," replied Little Bear's-Son. " Wilt thou come with me ? It is merrier with companionship. Thou art of a goodly size and shouldst be a man of strength."

[1] Mustache-man.

"As for that," said the giant, "my strength is nothing. For a really strong man, they say thou must go to him who is named Ivashko Medvedko."

"That is my name," said Little Bear's-Son.

"Then will I go with thee right willingly," said the other, and he left off his fishing and they journeyed on together.

They travelled for a day, when they came to a valley in which a giant four yards tall was at work. He was carrying earth thither, a whole hill at a time, and mending the roads with it.

"Health to thee," said Little Bear's-Son. "What art thou called?"

"Health to thee," replied the giant. "My name is Gorynia.[1] Whither doth God lead you?"

"Whither our eyes look," said Little Bear's-Son. "Thou art a strong man, I see. But why dost thou toil so hard?"

"Because I am dull," answered the other. "There is no war and the Tzardom is at peace; so, having nothing to do, I amuse myself. But as for strength, I have little enough compared with a certain youth named Ivashko Medvedko."

"I am he," said Little Bear's-Son.

[1] Hill-man.

"Then take me with you," said the giant, "and I will be thy younger brother." And he left his road-making and journeyed on with the others.

They travelled for two days, when they passed through a forest of oak-trees, and in it they perceived a third giant as tall as a barn, at work making all the oaks of the same height. If one was too tall, he drove it further into the earth with a blow of his fist, and if too short, he pulled it up to the proper level.

"Health to thee!" said Little Bear's-Son. "Thou art indeed a mighty man. What is thy name?"

"Health to thee!" responded the giant. "My name is Dubynia.[1] But my strength is as naught compared with that of a certain Ivashko Medvedko that I have heard tell of."

"I am that one," said Little Bear's-Son. "Wilt thou go with us and be our comrade?"

"That I will," answered the giant. "Whither doth your path lead?"

"Whither our eyes look," said Little Bear's-Son, and the third giant left his work in the oak-forest and went with them.

They travelled, all four together, for three days,

---

[1] Oak-man.

when they came to a wilderness full of all kinds of game, and Little Bear's-Son said : " Of what profit is it for us to wander further through the white world ? Let us build a house here and dwell in ease and comfort."

The three giants agreed. All immediately set to work clearing the stubble and preparing the timbers and before nightfall the dwelling was completed. It was built of the hugest trees and was big enough to shelter comfortably forty ordinary men. When it was finished they made a hunt and killed and snared beasts and fowl to fill their larder.

The next morning Little Bear's-Son said : " Each day three of us must hunt so that we lack not food, while the fourth stays at home to guard our house and to cook for the rest. Let us cast lots, therefore, to see who shall stay at home to-day." They cast lots and it fell to Usynia, he of the huge mustache, to remain, and the other three went away to hunt.

When they had departed Usynia took flesh and fowl and prepared a fit meal for his comrades when they should return, and boiled and baked and roasted whatever pleased his soul. When all was ready he washed his head, and sitting down under the window, began to comb his curly locks with a comb.

Suddenly it thundered, the wind began to moan, the earth began to shake and the wild, thick, silent forest bent down to the ground. Usynia grew faint and giddy and everything seemed to turn green. As he looked out of the window, he saw the earth begin to rise, and from under it lifted a huge stone, and from beneath the stone came a Baba-Yaga, riding in a great iron mortar, driving with the pestle and sweeping away her trail behind her with a kitchen-broom.

Usynia was badly frightened but he opened the door, and when the old witch came in, wished her good health and gave her a bench to sit on.

"Canst thou not see, thou great lump," snarled the Baba-Yaga, "that I am hungry? Give me to eat!"

Usynia took a roast duck from the oven and some bread and salt, and set them before her. She ate all greedily and demanded more. He brought another piece of meat, but it was so small that she flew into a rage. "Is this how thou servest me?" she cried, and seizing him with her bony arms, she dragged him from side to side of the room, bumped his head on the floor, beat him almost to death with her iron pestle and threw him under the table. Then she cut a strip of skin from his back, snatched everything out of the oven and ate it, bones and all, and drove away in her mortar.

When the bruised giant came to his senses, he tied his handkerchief about his head and sat groaning till his comrades returned.

Seeing, they asked : " Art thou in pain, that thou hast bound up thy head ? And where is our supper ?"

"Ah, little brothers," he replied, " I have been able neither to boil nor to roast for you. The oven is new and the smoke poured out into the room till it gave me a headache." So Little Bear's-Son and his two comrades prepared their meals themselves.

The next day Gorynia remained at home. He roasted and fried to his heart's content, and when all was done, he washed his head and began to comb his hair, when all at once it lightened, hail began to fall and the trees of the dense, sleepy forest bent over to the ground. He grew faint and giddy and everything seemed to turn green. Then he saw the earth stir, the stone lift, and from beneath it the Baba-Yaga came riding in her mortar, driving with the pestle and sweeping away her trail with her kitchen-broom.

Gorynia was too frightened to hide himself, and the old witch came in without knocking. " Health to thee, grandmother !" said the giant, and bade her sit down.

" Dost thou not see that I am hungry and thirsty ?" she snapped. " Fetch me food !"

He set a piece of venison and a cup of *kwas* before her.

She ate and drank and asked for more, and he brought her another piece of meat. This, however, being smaller than the first, did not please her fancy. " Is it thus thou servest me ?" she shrieked, and gripping him by the hair with her skinny hands, she dragged him from corner to corner, beat his head against the walls and belaboured him with her iron pestle till his senses left him. Then she cut a strip of flesh from his back, threw him under the bench, ate all that he had cooked and drove away.

When the others returned from their hunting, they found Gorynia sitting with his head bandaged and groaning louder than had Usynia the day before. " Alas, little brothers !" he said, when they

questioned him, "the wood was damp and would
not burn, and from trying to bake and roast for
you, my head aches as if it would burst!" So the
three cooked their own supper and went to bed.

The next day Dubynia was left at home, while
the others hunted, and to him the same thing
happened also. The Baba-Yaga appeared, beat
him black and blue with her pestle, cut a strip of
flesh from his back, threw him into a corner, ate the
supper and drove away. He also sat groaning till
the others returned, when he said : " Little brothers,
I have been able neither to boil nor to bake for
you, for the dampers of the stove would not close,
and the gas from the burning wood made me giddy
and caused my poor little head to ache as if it must
split in two !" So the others got themselves something to eat and went to sleep.

On the fourth day it came the turn of Little
Bear's-Son to stay. He put the house to rights,
boiled, baked and roasted, and when all was
prepared, washed his head, sat down under the
window and began to comb his hair. Suddenly
rain began to fall, the forest complained and bowed
down and everything turned green before his eyes ;
then the earth parted, the great stone tilted, and

out from the hole came the Baba-Yaga, riding in her mortar, driving with her pestle and sweeping out her path behind her with the kitchen-broom.

Little Bear's-Son was not frightened, however, nor was he made giddy. He fetched his iron club of twenty-five *poods*, stood it ready in a corner and opened the door. " Health to thee, grandmother !" he said.

She hobbled in and sat down, grinding all her teeth and smiling. " Fool !" she said. " Why dost thou not offer me something to eat and drink ? Canst thou not see that I am famished ?"

" The food that I have cooked," he replied, " is for my comrades, not for thee !"

The old witch snatched up her pestle and sprang upon him, thinking to treat him as she had the others, but he seized her by her grey locks, grasped his iron club, and began to beat her till even her witch's body suffered tortures and she howled for mercy. He stayed not his hand, however, till she was half dead. Then he threw her into a cupboard and locked the door.

Presently the three giants returned, expecting, each one of them, to find Little Bear's-Son well beaten and their supper gone. But he welcomed them, bade them sit down and brought from the oven foods of all sorts, deliciously cooked and in plenty. The giants ate and drank their fill, each one saying to himself: " Surely the Baba-Yaga did not come to our brother to-day !"

When the supper was ended, Little Bear's-Son heated the bath for his comrades and all went to bathe. Now, because the witch had cut the strips of flesh from their backs, each of the three giants tried to stand always with his face toward Little Bear's-Son, lest he see the scar. So at length he asked: " Brothers, why do ye stand thus facing me, like men who fear to show their shoulders?" They turned themselves about, then, and he asked: " Why are the scars upon your backs?"

Then Usynia said: " The day I stayed at home the smoke of the fire blinded my eyes, so that I touched the stove and the hot iron seared me." Gorynia said: " When I remained, the wood was damp, and in filling the stove with dry, a faggot dropped from my shoulder and tore my flesh." And Dubynia said: " When I was left behind, the gas from the oven made me giddy so that I slipped and fell upon thine iron club."

Then Little Bear's-Son laughed, and opening the

cupboard door, dragged from thence the Baba-
Yaga. "Here, my brothers," he said, "are the
smoke, the dampness, and the gas."

Now the old witch was cunning, and she pretended to be still senseless from her beating. She
opened one eye a little, however, and seeing her
chance, suddenly leaped into her mortar, whirled
through the doorway, and in another moment had
disappeared beneath the huge stone.

The three giants, angered to find their secret
discovered, were still more furious to see the Baba-
Yaga outwit them. They ran to the stone and
put forth all their strength to turn it, but were
unable. Then Little Bear's-Son went to the stone,
lifted it and hurled it a *verst* away. Beneath it
was a great dark hole, like the burrow of an
enormous fox.

"Brothers," said Little Bear's-Son, "the witch is
in this abyss. She is now our mortal enemy and
if we do not kill her, she will drive us, one by one,
out of the white world. Which of us shall follow
her?"

The three giants, however, had tasted the Baba-
Yaga's power and had no relish for attacking her
under the ground. Dubynia hid behind Gorynia

THE BABA-YAGA CAME RIDING IN HER MORTAR, DRIVING WITH THE PESTLE AND SWEEPING AWAY HER TRAIL
WITH THE KITCHEN BROOM.

and Gorynia slunk behind Usynia and Usynia looked up at the blue sky as if he had not heard. " Well," said Little Bear's-Son, " it seems that I must be the one to go." He bade them, then, cut into strips the hides of the beasts they had trapped and killed, and to twist the strips into a long rope. He planted a great post in the ground, tied one end of the rope to this and threw the other end into the dark hole. " Now, little brothers," he said, "remain here and watch, one of you at a time. If ye see the rope quiver and shake, lay hold of it straightway and hoist me out."

Little Bear's-Son put food in his pouch, bade the giants farewell and grasping the hide-rope, lowered himself into the yawning abyss. Whether it was a long way or a short way, the rope held and was sufficient and at length he reached the bottom. There he found a trodden path which led him through a long underground passage, till finally he emerged into another world—the world that lies under the earth. He found there a sun and moon, tall trees and wide rivers and green meadows like those of the upper world, but there were no human beings to be seen, nothing but great birds flying in flocks.

He wandered a day, and two, and three, and on the fourth day he came, in a forest, to a wretched little hut standing on fowls' legs and turning round and round without ceasing. About it was a garden and in the garden was a beautiful damsel plucking flowers.

He greeted her and she said : " Health to thee, good youth, but what dost thou here ? This is the house of a Baba-Yaga, who if thou remainest will surely devour thee !"

" It is she I seek," he answered.

" Thou art a brave man," the damsel said. " But the witch is a hundred times more powerful here, where she is surrounded by her enchantments, than in the upper-world. She is now asleep but presently she will wake and ride away. Hide thou in the forest till she is gone and I will show thee a way by which, perchance, thou mayest overcome her. Only promise truly that if thou dost succeed, thou wilt take me back with thee to the white world whence she carried me away."

Little Bear's-Son gave the maiden this promise, and concealed himself in the forest, and after a while he felt the ground rumble and saw the trees shiver and bow down, and out of the hut came the Baba-Yaga, riding away in her great iron mortar, driving with the pestle and sweeping out her trail behind her with her kitchen-broom. When she was out of sight, he hastened to the hut and the damsel, taking him into the cellar, showed him two great casks full of water, one on the right side and the other on the left.

"Drink," she bade him, "from the right cask, as much as thou canst hold."

He stooped down and took a long drink, when she asked : "How strong art thou now?"

"I am so strong," he answered, "that with one finger I could lift and carry away this cask."

"Drink again," she commanded.

Again he drank. "Now," she asked, "how much strength is in thee?"

"I am so strong," he replied, "that if I chose, with one hand I could lift and turn about this whole hut!"

"Listen well," she said, "to what I tell thee. The cask from which thou hast drunk contains Strong Water. It is this which gives the Baba-Yaga her strength. The cask on the left holds Weak Water, and whoever drinks from it is made quickly powerless. As soon as the witch appears, seize tightly her pestle before she lays it down, and loose not thy grip as thou lovest thy life. She will try to shake thee off, but thou art now so strong that she will not be able to do so. Failing in this, she will hasten here to drink of the Strong Water. Change, therefore, now, the two casks and put each in the place of the other, so that she will be deceived and will drink of the Weak Water, and then thou mayest kill her. When thou drawest thy sword, however, strike but a single stroke. Her mortar, her pestle, and her broom, all her faithful servants, will cry out to thee to strike again, but if thou strikest a second stroke, she will instantly come to life again. Beware also to draw thy sword before she has drunk of the Weak Water, for until then it will be powerless against her spells."

Little Bear's-Son immediately changed the places of the two casks, putting the right one on the left hand and the Weak Water where the Strong Water had been. And soon, as he conversed with the lovely maiden in the garden, the trees began to sob and the timbers of the hut to creak, and the Baba-Yaga came riding home. Little Bear's-Son hid himself behind a hedge and the old witch stopped and leaped down from her mortar.

" Poo! poo!" she cried, smelling around her.
"I smell a Russian smell! Who has visited here?"

" No one, grandmother," said the damsel. " How
could one from the upper-world find his way here?"

" Well," said the Baba-Yaga, " I fear no one here
save a Russian named Ivashko Medvedko, and he
is so far away at this moment that it would take a
he-crow a year to fly hither with one of his bones."

" Thou liest, old witch!" cried Little Bear's-Son,
and with the words sprang out and seized hold of
her iron pestle. The Baba-Yaga whistled and spat
and howled with rage, but try as she might, she
could not shake him off. She tore away in a whirlwind, over the tree-tops of the forest, striving to
dash him down to pieces. She whirled him high
over a broad river, trying to fling him down to
drown, threatening him with all dreadful tortures.
But Little Bear's-Son held on with all the strength
he had gained from drinking the Strong Water, and
she could not break his hold. She dragged him
back and forth over the whole under-world in vain,
till at length even she grew tired. Then back she
flew to the hut and dropping her pestle, pounced
down into the cellar and began to drink from the
cask on the right hand.

Hardly, however, had the Baba-Yaga rushed from the cellar to attack Little Bear's-Son again, than she became all at once as weak as a blade of grass, and drawing his sword, with a single blow, he cut off her wicked old head.

Instantly the iron mortar and pestle and the kitchen-broom cried out to him: " Strike again ! Strike again !" But, remembering what the damsel had said, he answered: " A brave man's sword strikes not twice," and sheathed it.

Little Bear's-Son made a great fire in the forest and burned the witch's body to ashes. Then, taking the lovely maiden with him, he set out on his return to the upper-world.

For two days they journeyed, and on the second day rain began to fall, so that they took refuge under a tree. Near by Little Bear's-Son saw a great bird's-nest with fledglings in it, and pitying the young ones, which were being drenched, he hung his cloak above the nest to protect them. Presently the rain ceased and they went on till they reached the underground passage and followed it to the place where the hide-rope hung. Little Bear's-Son tied the damsel to its end and shook it, and one of the three giants, who was watching above, ran to fetch the other two and they began to pull up the rope.

When they saw the beauty of the maiden, however, the three giants were envious of their comrade and each wished her for his wife. So they agreed together and when they had hoisted Little Bear's-Son, in his turn, almost to the top, they cut the rope and let him fall and straightway began to quarrel over which of them should marry her.

Little Bear's-Son was terribly hurt by his fall, but so strong had he become that he was not killed. He lay on his back one day, he lay on his side two days and three, and then he managed to walk through the long passage into the under-world again. While he wandered there, wondering what he should do, there came flying one of the huge birds whose flocks he had seen, and alighting near him, it spoke to him with a human voice.

" Thou didst have pity on my fledglings, Ivashko Medvedko," it said, " and in return for this I will serve thee a service. Ask of me what thou wilt."

" If thou art able," replied Little Bear's-Son, " take me out into the white world."

" It is a hard service," said the bird, " but there is a way I know and I will carry thee. The

journey, however, will take three months. Go now
into the forest and snare much game and twist a
wicker basket and fill it. Mount my back with
this and whenever I turn my head as I fly, feed me."

Little Bear's-Son did as he was bidden. He
made a great basket, filled it with game and
mounted with it to the back of the huge bird,
which at once rose into the air and flew away like
a hurricane. It flew day after day, without stopping. As often as it turned its head, he fed it with
some of the game from the basket, and when it had
flown for three months and the basket was almost
empty, it carried him out into the white world, set
him down in a grassy meadow, bade him farewell
and flew away.

Whether it was a long way or a short way, Little
Bear's-Son came at length to his own Tzardom and
to the forest wherein stood the house that he and
the three giants had built. A little way within the
forest he saw a green lawn and on it a lovely girl
was tending cows. He drew near and found to his
surprise that she was none other than the damsel
he had rescued from the hut of the Baba-Yaga.

She greeted him with joy and told him all that
had befallen her : how the giants had quarrelled

over her, how they had fought each day for an hour, but as no one of them was stronger than another, had not been able to decide and had made her tend their cattle till one should prevail. Then he kissed her on the mouth and said he : " Thou shalt wed no one of those faithless brothers of mine, but I will wed thee myself."

Little Bear's-Son sent her on before him, and coming to the hut where the three giants sat at the window drinking, pulled his cap over his face and in a humble tone asked for a drink of *kwas*.

" Be off with thee !" grunted Usynia, without turning his head.

" We want no beggars here !" snarled Gorynia.

" *Kwas*, forsooth !" shouted Dubynia. " Thou shalt have a taste of my club instead !"

Then Little Bear's-Son took off his cap and they recognized him. They turned pale with fright and making for the door, ran away as if the Tartars were after them, and were never seen in that Tzardom again. And Little Bear's-Son married the lovely damsel and they dwelt in that house all their lives in such peace and comfort that they wanted nothing they did not have and had nothing they did not want.

WASSILY THE UNLUCKY

WASSILY THE UNLUCKY

THERE lived in a certain town a merchant who was seven hundred times richer than anyone else, so that there was no wealth in the whole Tzardom to be compared with his. Whatever business he embarked upon prospered exceedingly and all that he handled seemed to turn to gold, so that people called him "Marko the Rich." God had granted him no sons and but one daughter, as sweet as sweet clover, who was named Anasthasia and who was five years old.

For all his wealth, Marko the Rich was mean and flint-hearted. He gave as stingily as might be to the Church and to the poor. He could not bear to see a beggar and did one but approach his windows, he would order his servants to loose his fierce wolf-hounds and set the beasts upon him. For this reason he was feared and hated throughout all the country-side.

285

One evening three little old men, huddled in rags, with white hair and long white beards, came to the window to beg a crust of bread and a place to sleep. The merchant saw them and would have set the dogs upon them as usual, but Anasthasia, his little daughter, interceded for them and besought her father to let them, at least, sleep in the stable with the horses. Marko the Rich grumblingly agreed to this and she ran before them to the stalls, showed them where was clean hay to lie upon and wished them a good-night.

The little girl woke next morning before sunrise and wondering how the beggars fared, jumped out of bed, dressed herself and saying her prayer, ran to the stable and climbing to the loft, looked down upon them. To her surprise she saw that they seemed to be poor beggars no longer but were clad in splendid robes of rich brocade, like Bishops, and had crowns upon their heads and strange books in their hands.

While she looked one of the old men said to the others: "Brothers, what do ye read is befalling at this moment?"

The second answered: "Brother, in the next village to this, at the hut of the peasant called Ivan, a son is being born."

The first said : "We will give him the name of Wassily and let him be called the Unlucky. But what inheritance shall we grant him ?"

And the third replied : " Let him have for his own all the wealth of Marko the Rich in whose stable we have spent the night." Having so spoken, they said a prayer before the holy images and left the place, while little Anasthasia, wondering at their strange words, ran back to the house, woke her father and told him what she had seen and heard.

The merchant was troubled and sent messengers after the three old men, but they could not be found ; and at length, desiring to learn if by any possibility there could have been truth in their words, he ordered horses to be put to his gorgeous sledge and drove post-haste to the next village, where he went to the priest and inquired whether a child had been born there that morning.

" A son has indeed been born to the poorest serf in the village," answered the priest. " I myself named him Wassily, but I have not yet baptized him, since, on account of the father's poverty, no one is willing to be godfather to the poor child."

" I will be his godfather," said Marko the Rich,

and went out and ordered food and drink and
made a plenteous feast and bade them bring the
babe.   So the parents brought him and he was
baptized and all feasted and made merry to their
heart's content.   On the next day Marko the Rich
drove again to the village and stopping at the hut
of the poor peasant, spoke kindly to him and
flattered him.   " Peasant," he said, " thou art a
miserably poor man without stick or stone of thine
own or wherewith to support thy family, and thou
canst not properly care for this little son of thine.
Why not give him to me ?   I will bring him up in
a decent manner and as for thee, his father, I will
give thee, for thy living, a thousand *roubles*."

The poor serf pondered the matter well, and at
last allowed himself to be persuaded.   The merchant, accordingly, gave him the one thousand
roubles, took the babe, wrapped him warmly in his
own coat of fox-fur, got into his sledge and drove
away.

Now it was winter-time, the season of greatest
cold, and the ground was covered deep with snow.
After they had gone several *versts* from the village,
Marko the Rich stopped the sledge, gave the child
to his trusty driver and bade him throw him into a

deep ravine whose steep brink they were passing.
The man did as he was bidden, and the merchant,
as he saw the helpless babe hurled into the
depths, called after him mockingly: "There, thou
beggarly brat! Thou art right welcome now to
possess my wealth and to dispose of it as thou
wilt!"

On the third day thereafter, as it happened, a
company of tradesmen came driving along that
same road, bringing to Marko the Rich a sum of
money which they owed him. When they came
opposite the ravine they thought they heard the
cry of a child. They stopped their sledges while
they listened attentively and one of them sent his
driver to search, and the man, climbing down the
steep precipice, at the bottom, among the gloomy
rocks, found the babe, wrapped in the fox-furs,
alive and unhurt. He carried the child to his
master and the tradesman brought it to the town
and to the house of Marko the Rich.

The merchant, seeing the babe, began to question
them and when they had told how they had found
him, knew at once that it was the little Wassily,
his godchild. He took the infant in his arms and
after holding it a while, handed it to his daughter,

saying : " There, Anasthasia, there is something for thee to nurse and to play with." He began then to regale his guests with all manner of delicious foods and wines, and when they had feasted and drunk until they were in high humour, he said to them : " Ye are but humble tradesmen and no doubt lack not children of your own. Give the foundling to me and let him be a companion to my little daughter and I will bring him up in a fitting manner."

The merchant who had the child would not at first agree, but when the rich man said, " Do this and I forgive all thy indebtedness to me," the others added their persuasions and he consented. So the waif was again left with Marko the Rich, to the delight of Anasthasia, who at once fetched a cradle, hung it with new embroidered curtains and began to care for the little boy, never parting from him by day or night.

One day passed, and two, and three. On the third night a tempest arose and the merchant, waiting till his little daughter was asleep, took the babe from her side, put him into an open boat and pushed the boat into the sea-ocean. The storm, however, passed over and did not break, and the skiff swam safely with its burden till it neared a rocky island on which was a monastery.

It chanced that one of the monks, going in the morning to fetch a bucket of salt water, saw the floating boat, brought it to shore and took the babe to the Abbot. The Abbot named him Wassily. " And," said he, " since we find him in such an evil case, let us call him the Unlucky !" So from that day the boy was known as Wassily the Unlucky, and remained at the monastery, loved of all the monks, till he was eighteen years of age and had learned to read and write and to be clever. The Abbot in especial was fond of him and at length made him the monastery's purse-bearer and trusted him in all things.

Now once each year Marko the Rich was accustomed to journey to another Tzardom to collect money that was owed to him and on one of these trips the vessel which carried him by chance cast anchor at the monastery, where the merchant spent the night. There he was received like the rich man he was : the chapel was lighted with many candles and the Abbot summoned the monks to sing and read the holy service. Noticing among them one young man who was more sturdy and

comely than all his fellows, the visitor asked his
name.

" We call him Wassily the Unlucky," replied the
Abbot.

" A strange name," said the merchant. " Why
is he so called ?"

Thereupon the Abbot told of the finding of the
babe so many years before in the open boat and
then Marko the Rich knew that the lad was his
own godchild, whom twice he had tried to drive
out of the white world. He pondered deeply in
his evil mood till the service was ended, when he
said to the Abbot : " How much should I like to
possess such a clever, handsome lad as yours! If I
but had him, I would appoint him at once my
chief clerk, entrust all my affairs to his manage-
ment and make him a rich man. Couldst thou
not put him in my care ?"

The Abbot thought over this a long time, excus-
ing himself on one pretext or another when the
merchant pressed him to answer. Finally, however, Marko the Rich offered him a sum of twenty-
five thousand *roubles* with which to rebuild the
monastery. " Surely," urged he, " this is but God's
manner of repaying to you the charity ye have

given to a foundling. As for him, he will find a good home with me, I promise."

The Abbot consulted the monks and at length it was agreed to let Wassily the Unlucky go. He called the lad accordingly, told him his decision and gave him into the charge of the merchant, who bade him go to the town in which he lived and carry an important letter to his wife, while he himself continued his journey. And the sealed letter which Marko the Rich sent by his hand read thus:

"Marko the Merchant to his wife: As soon as my messenger brings thee this letter, prepare at once in the kitchen a great caldron of boiling lye. Call him then to thee and when he doth pass the caldron, push him into it, so that he may die. Do this without fail, for this youth works evil against me. If thou dost not, beware my punishment!"

Wassily the Unlucky took the letter, said farewell with tears to the Abbot and the monks, and quitting the island, set out on his way to the home of his new master. Whether the time was long or short, whether the road was rough or smooth, he came at length one night to a wood in which was no human habitation and no building save a poor shed for cows. He entered this to sleep and found

within it three little old beggar-men with white
hair and long white beards.

He shared his bread with them and when they
had conversed for some time all fell asleep, and as
he slept Wassily dreamed a dream. The three
little old men seemed to be beggar-men no longer,
but were clad in robes of splendid brocade, with
crowns on their heads and curious leathern books
in their hands. As he wondered at this, he thought
one of the old men said to the others: "Brothers,
whither goeth this youth?"

The second answered: "Brother, to the house of
Marko the Rich, to carry a letter from the
merchant to his wife."

"What saith the letter?" asked the first.

The second replied: "It bids his wife prepare a
huge kettle of boiling lye and push the youth into
it, so that he may die. How shall we bring this
evil to naught?"

"Brothers, I will alter the message," said the third,
and taking the letter, he blew upon it, saying:
"Let him now carry it without fear, for God will
not abandon him."

In his dream Wassily the Unlucky had heard
this conversation with tears, saying to himself:

" What have I done, then, that the merchant should
desire my cruel death ?"   And when he woke he
was glad to think it had been but a dream.   The
three little old men had already departed, and feel-
ing the letter safe in his pocket, he went on his way
to the town of Marko the Rich.

So he came to the merchant's house and gave
the letter to his wife.   And when she had broken
the seal and opened it, she read thus :

" Marko the Merchant to his wife : As soon
as my messenger brings thee this letter, prepare at
once a festival.   Call the priest and the neighbours
to thee and when they are come, marry him
straightway to our daughter Anasthasia.   Do this
without fail, for this youth shall be my heir.   If
thou dost not, beware my punishment !"

The wife at once called her daughter, read her
the letter and brought her to the youth, and each
loved each other from that moment.   She bade the
cooks bake and roast and the serving-men fetch
beer and wine for the festival, swept and garnished
the house, dressed the lovely Anasthasia in her
richest apparel, adorned her with jewels and sent
for the priest and the neighbours.   That same
night Wassily the Unlucky and the merchant's

daughter were brought under the golden crown,[1] and they remained at the house of Marko the Rich and for some months lived happily together.

One day news was brought that the merchant was returning by ship, and his wife, with her daughter and son-in-law, hastened to the dock to meet him. When Marko the Rich saw them, however, and learned that Wassily the Unlucky was now the husband of his daughter, he flew into a violent passion and calling his wife aside, demanded how she had dared disobey his express command.

She replied that she had but carried out his written instruction and when he had examined the letter he had sent her, he was compelled to admit that it was in his own handwriting. He swallowed his rage, therefore, for the time, and began to plan how he might destroy his son-in-law without fail.

They lived together one month, they lived together two, and three, when one day Marko the Rich called Wassily the Unlucky to him and bade him prepare to journey at once across three times nine countries to the thirtieth realm. "In this realm," he said, "is the Tzardom of Tzar Zmey.

[1] A golden crown is used in the Greek marriage ceremony.

THE VESSEL WHICH CARRIED HIM . . . . CAST ANCHOR AT THE MONASTERY.

Go to him and bid him pay thee, for me, the sum
he owes for rent during the past twelve years, since
he has built his Palace on land which is mine.
When this is accomplished, inquire concerning
twelve of my ships which were lost upon his coasts
some three years since and from which no tidings
have come. See to it that thou start by sunrise
to-morrow."

Anasthasia, when she heard, wept bitterly and
tried to dissuade her father, but in vain. So next
morning Wassily the Unlucky said a prayer to
God, bade his wife farewell and with a store of
biscuits in his knapsack, mounted his good horse
and set out on his journey.

Whether the way was long or short, whether the
Tzardom of Tzar Zmey was far or near, he came
at length to its border. Here was a wide river on
which an old ferryman plied back and forth. He
rode aboard and crossed to the other side, when
the ferryman asked: "Whither art thou faring, my
friend?"

"I go to Tzar Zmey," he replied, "to ask of him
money he owes my little father-in-law for rental of
land on which he has built his Palace."

"Well," said the ferryman, "it will take a smart

lad to get it.   Wilt thou serve me a service with
Tzar Zmey ?"

"Gladly," answered Wassily.

"Then," said the ferryman, "when thou comest
before him, if thou hast opportunity, remind him
that now for thirty years he has condemned me to
ferry people back and forth across this river.   Ask
of him, I pray thee, whether I shall have to labour
thus for thirty years more, or if not, when I shall
be free to go whither I will.   Wilt thou do this for
me ?"

Wassily the Unlucky promised and resumed his
journey, and before long he came to an arm of the
sea-ocean, across which lay stranded a huge whale-
fish.   A thick forest was growing on its tail and on
its back was a village whose peasants ploughed up
and down its sides with their iron ploughs and drove
sharpened stakes into its flesh.   Boys had made a
playground between its eyes and on its moustache
girls picked mushrooms.   Wassily rode across on
the whale-fish, his horse's hoofs pounding on its
ribs, and when he reached the other side the
monster opened its wide mouth, sighing bitterly.

"A good journey to thee, my friend," it said.
"Whither goest thou ?"

"To Tzar Zmey," answered Wassily, "to get money he owes my little father-in-law."

"Well," said the whale-fish, "thou art a clever lad if thou dost not fail! Wilt thou serve me a service with Tzar Zmey?"

"Cheerfully," Wassily replied.

"When thou seest him, then," said the whale-fish, "if thou hast opportunity, say to him that I have been lying here in this torture for three years, where wayfarers, on horse and afoot, wear my body to my ribs. Beg him to show me mercy and ask whether my disgrace and punishment is to last three years more, or if not, when I shall be free to swim where I will. Wilt thou say this?"

Wassily the Unlucky gave the whale-fish his promise and rode on till he came to a green meadow on which stood a great Palace of white stone. No sentries were on guard at the gate nor any watchman at the door, and he left his horse to graze on the meadow and entered.

Within the Palace all was still and he saw no one. He went through one room after another, finding each more beautiful than the last, till he came to the inmost chamber of all, and here, sitting on a chair, he found a beautiful damsel weeping.

"Health to thee, lovely maiden !" he said.

"And to thee," she answered. "But what manner of man art thou? How didst thou come into this dreadful place? Knowest thou not that this is the abode of Tzar Zmey, the Serpent-Tzar, who devours a man at every meal?"

Wassily the Unlucky told her his errand, whereat the girl exclaimed: "Well that thou hast seen me first! Thou hast been sent here not to fetch money from him, but in order that he may devour thee. Never mind, I shall save thy life. But tell me, by what road didst thou travel and what didst thou see on thy way?"

So he related to her how he had met the ferryman and the whale-fish and what each had asked, and while they were yet conversing, the ground on which the Palace stood began to shiver and its walls to rumble and shake. "The Serpent-Tzar is coming!" she cried. "Thou must hide at once!" She showed him a coffer beneath the bed, made him lie down in it and shut its lid. "Listen," she said, "and thou shalt hear whatever the Snake says to me."

Presently Tzar Zmey, in the form of a huge serpent, came rolling into the room. "I smell a Russian smell!" he said. "Who has been here?"

The damsel laughed, and said she: "Would a Russian by any chance dare to venture into the innermost room of thy Palace? Thou hast been flying about all day in Russia and thou thyself hast brought the odour with thee!"

The Serpent-Tzar was satisfied and began to kiss and fondle her without stint, and then, coiling his scaly length on the bed, he said: "I am tired. Come, my darling, and rub my head so that I may go to sleep." So she began to rub his head, and as she did so, she said: "My Tzar, while thou wert absent I had such a curious dream! Wouldst thou hear it?"

"Yes," he said.

"I dreamed," she told him, "that I was walking along a highroad and where it crossed an arm of the sea-ocean there lay stranded a huge whale-fish so that people on horses and afoot crossed upon his body. And the monster spoke to me and asked me how much longer it must needs endure that torture and how soon it should be free?"

Then Tzar Zmey drowsily answered her. "It shall lie there until it vomits forth again, whole

and sound, twelve ships which it swallowed without my permission three years since in the middle
of the sea-ocean."

The girl said: "Then in my dream I went on
till I came to a broad river, where a ferryman plied
back and forth. And when he had ferried me over
he asked me how much longer he would be made
so to labour, and when he should be free."

Tzar Zmey, half asleep, answered: "Let him
only take into his boat the first who comes, and,
leaping out himself, push the boat out into the
stream. Then will the newcomer be compelled
to ferry in his place for ever."

Having thus spoken, the Serpent-Tzar fell fast
asleep and snored till the walls trembled, when the
girl opened the coffer and Wassily the Unlucky
thanked her and left the Palace. He caught his
horse on the meadow, mounted and hastened back
the way he had come. When he came to the arm
of the sea-ocean and began to cross on the whale-
fish, the monster saw him and opening its wide
jaws, called out: "Well, friend, didst thou serve
me the service with Tzar Zmey?"

"Yes," said Wassily.

"And what said he?" asked the whale-fish.

"Wait till I am over," said Wassily, "and I will

tell thee." So he crossed, and as soon as he came
to the other side he mounted on its tail and cried
with a loud voice : "O ye villagers and wayfarers,
ye who would not be suddenly overwhelmed, leave
this place without delay, for the sea-ocean is about
to cover it!" Hearing, the wayfarers hastened and
the peasants left their ploughing and the children
their playing and mushroom-gathering, and ran to
their houses and loaded their carts with all their
belongings and carried them to a distance, till the
whale-fish was as deserted as if the Tartars were
coming.

Then Wassily the Unlucky shouted : "O whale-
fish! this punishment has been thine because three
years since thou didst swallow, without Tzar Zmey's
permission, twelve ships in the blue sea-ocean, and
thou shalt be set free only when thou dost vomit
them forth unharmed." So saying, he spurred his
horse and leaped from the tail of the whale-fish to
the shore.

He had need to hasten, for when it heard, the
monster began to move as if a hill were turning
over. It thrashed the water into foam and vomited
forth, one after the other, the twelve ships. The
sailors rejoiced to see the white world again : they
shouted and blew on trumpets, put up their sails

and showed a flag at each masthead. On each ship a priest was chanting the *Te Deum*, and altogether there was such a roar of gladness that it waked the whole sea-ocean.

As soon as the ships appeared the whale-fish found itself free and with a mighty splash it plunged into deep water. Then from the waves it opened its huge mouth and cried to Wassily: "What service shall I serve thee, my friend, and how shall I repay thee? Wilt thou have great pearls, or the bright-coloured stones that ships carry?"

"If thou wilt," answered Wassily, "I will have as thy gift some of the bright-coloured stones."

The whale dropped to the bottom of the sea-ocean like a key, and came back with an enamelled chest in its mouth, and in the chest were jewels whose value and brightness cannot be told in words, finer than are to be found in the treasuries of all the Tzars together.

Wassily the Unlucky called to him the captain of the ships, and asked: "Whose ships are ye and whither go ye?"

They answered: "These are ships of Marko the Rich, to whom, when we were swallowed by the whale-fish, we were sailing with our cargoes."

"I am his son-in-law," he said. "Carry ye to him these jewels also."

They would have taken him aboard with them but he bade them await him at the mouth of the wide river that was the border of Tzar Zmey's Tzardom, and rode on to where the old ferryman plied in his boat.

"Well, friend," asked the ferryman, "didst thou serve me the service with Tzar Zmey?"

"Yes," replied Wassily.

"And what said he?" asked the ferryman.

"When I am over," he replied, "I will tell thee." So he crossed and as the boat came to the other side, he rode to its prow and said: "O ferryman, when the next one comes to cross, take him into thy boat and immediately push it out into the stream; then will he be compelled to ferry here in thy place for ever."

So saying, he leaped his horse to the shore and rode to the river's mouth, where the ships awaited him, and went on board and sailed to the town of Marko the Rich.

Now when they landed at the dock and messengers ran and told the merchant that Wassily the Unlucky had returned with the twelve lost ships, bringing with him such a great treasure of jewels that it could not be reckoned, he well-nigh lost his senses with rage. He pretended to welcome his son-in-law with joy, however, and said to himself: "I will send him again to Tzar Zmey and next time he shall not escape, for I will go myself and arrange all things beforehand."

So, as soon as the rejoicings were ended, he gave out that he must go himself upon a journey and called for horses and relays and departed. He rode a long way and he rode a short way, and coming at length to the broad river, ordered the old ferryman to carry him across.

But as soon as he had entered the boat, the ferryman pushed it out into the stream, shouting: "Now, whoever thou art, thou shalt take thy turn!" and went away rejoicing. And Marko the Rich found himself thus in the power of the Serpent-Tzar, and not knowing the secret, was compelled to ferry people over for ever.

So Wassily the Unlucky came to no harm and lived in peace, plenty and charity with the beautiful Anasthasia who could not love him enough, and in time inherited all the lands and treasures of Marko the Rich.

TZAREVICH PETR AND THE WIZARD

TZAREVICH PETR AND THE WIZARD

In old, olden times, when God's world was full of wizards and forest monsters and when the rivers ran with sweet milk, there lived a Tzar named Bel-Belianin with his Tzaritza and their three sons, Alexé, Dimitry and Petr, lads comely and clever, all three of them.

One day the Tzaritza, who had gone to walk on the open *steppe*, failed to return to the Palace, and though wide search was made, no trace could be found of her. She had disappeared as completely as if she had fallen into the water. Then Tzar Bel-Belianin called together his Ministers and Boyars, his sages, his grandees and councillors, and asked their advice, and when they had deliberated for three weeks, the eldest among them came before him and said:

"O Tzar's Majesty! it is clear that the Tzaritza has been spirited away by Kastchey, the most powerful of all the wizards. While his own realm and castle is beyond three times nine lands, he possesses strongholds many and various in other Tzardoms, and it has long been known that his most splendid Palaces are upon the tops of the highest, most inaccessible mountains in the next Tzardom to thine own. It is, however, bootless to war against him, for his Palaces are, each and every one, surrounded by enchantment, and Kastchey himself cannot be killed by mortal means, since he carries his life not in his body, but in a secret place that is known only to himself. We counsel thee, therefore, to choose another wife, for thy lost Tzaritza thou wilt never regain as long as the world lasteth."

The Tzar was deeply saddened by this speech. So much did he love his vanished Tzaritza that he would not choose another in her place, but sent criers into far kingdoms, offering wealth and honours to whomever would restore her to him. Daring heroes and great generals came in response from all sides, each promising valiant deeds, and Tzar Bel-Belianin bade each take from the royal treasury sufficient gold for his needs. But though scores arrived thus and rode away, there came no news of the missing Tzaritza.

One day, as the Tzar sat musing sadly and troubled at heart in his summer-house, his three sons came into the garden and not knowing that he was within hearing, began to converse. "Methinks our little father is bereft of his reason," said Alexé, the eldest. "These boasting heroes who come from afar are galloping off with all his treasures. He is a fool to put faith in them. I warrant I could do as well as they."

Dimitry, the second son, said: "Doubtless they are but sorry scoundrels who play upon our Tzarfather's credulity. With a tenth of the sum that has been given them I myself would find our little mother."

But Petr, the youngest, said: "Not so, my brothers. If Kastchey the Wizard has her, it will need a stout heart to bring her back, and who knoweth where that may be found? Would, however, that our little father would send us abroad to do our best!"

When the lads had left the garden, Tzar Bel-Belianin re-entered the Palace and summoned them to his presence. "My dear sons," he said, " ye know how the loss of thy mother oppresses my heart and soul. Many brave heroes have searched for her vainly and I am minded now to send one of ye forth. Thou, therefore, Alexé, who art my eldest, take my fatherly blessing, with as much gold and as many troops as thou requirest, and try thy fortune in the quest. If thou dost succeed, thou shalt inherit my Tzardom."

So, boasting much, Tzarevich Alexé took from the treasury a full purse and with fifty thousand soldiers armed with iron lances, set out from the capital. He rode one day, he rode one week, he rode a month, and two and three, asking questions of all he met, until he had passed beyond the borders of his father's Tzardom, but no one had heard of the lost Tzaritza or of the strongholds of Kastchey the Wizard. At length he came, through fen and morass, to a desert land where only earth and sky were to be seen and the sand was as hot as cinder-cakes, and here his host vanished one by one till but ten remained. Beyond the desert was a forest and on the skirt of the forest, in a patch of wild hemp and bramble, he came upon an old grey-beard, a yard tall, sitting on a stone.

" Health to thee, grandfather," said Tzarevich Alexé.

" Health to thee, Tzarevich," replied the old

man. " Where doth God carry thee ?   Art thou
come hither to shirk a task or to find one ?"

" To find one," answered Tzarevich Alexé. " I
seek the stronghold of Kastchey the Wizard, who
hath stolen away my little mother."

" Thou art on the right track," said the other,
" but thou wilt not be able to reach it."

" Why not ?" asked the Tzarevich.

" Because," said the gray-beard, " there are three
broad rivers between, over which thou must be
ferried, and the price asked is a great one."

Tzarevich Alexé threw the old man a piece of
money. " I have gold and to spare," he said
haughtily, and spurring forward, rode on to the
first of the three rivers.   There waited on its bank
a ferryman covered with scales of copper like a
tortoise, with a head like a cask and so huge of
stature that the horses that carried the Tzarevich's
ten men snorted with terror and turning, galloped
away with their riders.   The Tzarevich approached
trembling and asked : " O ferryman, wilt thou
ferry me over ?"

" If thou pay me my price," answered the ferryman.

" And what is thy price ?" asked the Tzarevich.

"I will bring thee back for naught," said the other, "but for carrying thee across, I shall strike off thy right hand."

Tzarevich Alexé saw the sharp sword girded at the ferryman's side and his rebellious head drooped lower than his broad shoulders. "Of small use to myself should I be without my good right hand," he thought. "Yet, if I succeed, I shall be Tzar, and a Tzardom is worth the price."

So he bade the other take him across and on the further side the ferryman drew his sword and struck off his right hand, and bemoaning its loss the Tzarevich spurred on alone. He rode one day, he rode two, and three, and came to the second river, and on its bank waited a ferryman as tall as a fir-tree, armoured with plates of silver and of such a countenance that Tzarevich Alexé's heart fainted for very fear, and turning, he struck spurs to his steed and rode back the way he had come, to his own Tzardom.

When he reached the capital, he entered the Palace, came to his father, and said: "Gracious Sir! I have searched, these months through, in many lands, till there remains not a single man of the great host I took with me, while I myself have

lost my right hand, but no trace of Kastchey the
Wizard or of the Tzaritza, my little mother, could
I find !"

Then Tzar Bel-Belianin embraced him and wept
over him and summoning his second son, said :
" My dear son Dimitry, take my blessing, with
gold and troops as much and many as thou wilt,
and go thou forth and try. And if thou dost
succeed, thou shalt have my Tzardom after me."

And Dimitry, vowing he would do better than
his brother, took a knapsack full of gold and a
hundred thousand soldiers officered by captains of
captains, and set out. He too came at length,
through swamp and bog, to the desert of hot sand,
and here his men vanished till there were left but a
score. And on the edge of the further forest, in
the acre of wild hemp and bramble, he came upon
an old woman, a yard tall, sitting on a stone.

" Health to thee, grandmother !" said he.

" And to thee, Tzarevich !" she answered.
" Where doth God carry thee ? Why comest thou
hither ? To escape a task or to meet one ?"

" To meet one," he replied. " I seek the retreat
of the Wizard Kastchey, who hath stolen away my
little mother."

"Thou goest in the right direction," the old woman said, "but all the same thou wilt never reach it."

"Why not?" asked the Tzarevich.

"Because," answered the old woman, "there are three wide rivers between, on each of which is a ferry, and the price asked thee will be great."

Tzarevich Dimitry threw her two pieces of gold. "I have a plenty of such," he said scornfully, and rode on to the river. When they saw the gigantic ferryman, however, with his frame covered with copper armour, the horses his twenty men rode, stricken with terror, galloped away and the Tzarevich approached him trembling. He too was ferried over at the cost of his right hand, and lamenting its loss, rode on alone to the second river. And there, though the fierce aspect of the ferryman made his horse sweat and his own heart shake, he approached and asked, "O ferryman, wilt thou ferry me over?"

"If thou wilt pay my price," answered the ferryman.

"And what is thy price?" asked the Tzarevich.

"I will bring thee back for naught," said the

other, "but for ferrying thee over, I shall strike off thy left foot."

The Tzarevich's bright head hung lower than his stalwart shoulders. "I have already given my right hand," he thought, "and a foot is not so much more when a Tzardom is the reward." So he bade the other carry him over and when they had crossed the ferryman drew his sword and struck off his left foot, and Tzarevich Dimitry rode on.

He went one day, and two, and three, and came to the third river, on whose bank stood a ferry-man as tall as a tower, with legs like buttresses, clad all in golden armour and with a face so fierce and terrible that the Tzarevich's courage died within him. So he turned his horse about and in mortal fear spurred back the way he had come to his own Tzardom. There, coming before his father, he said:

"Gracious Sir! I have wandered these many months through strange lands, till there is left not one of the great army I took with me. As for me, I have, as thou seest, lost my right hand and my left foot, but I found no sign of the Wizard or of my little mother, the Tzaritza!"

Tzar Bel-Belianin kissed him and grieved over him and then, sending for his youngest son, bade him also take what he required and go and search.

"I have need of neither gold nor army, little father," said Tzarevich Petr. "Give me only a horse of my own choosing and a sword fit for a hero."

His father bade him choose the best blade from his armoury and the finest steed in his stables. Tzarevich Petr went to the armoury accordingly and tested the blades for a month, till he had picked the keenest and the strongest; then he bade the stable grooms collect all the Tzar's stud-horses and drive them to the blue sea-ocean, and watched to see what they would do. One swam far out and began to wrestle with the waves till the water boiled and dashed against the shore as in a tempest, and him Tzarevich Petr chose. He took his father's blessing, girded on the keen sword, and mounting the horse, set out.

He rode for a day and a night, for a week, for one month and for three. He passed the quagmire and the fiery desert, and at the edge of the forest, in the plot of wild hemp and briar, met the little old man and the little old woman sitting on two stones. He told them of his errand and the grey-beard said : " Thou hast a keen sword and the horse of a hero, but all the same thou wilt not get to Kastchey."

" Why not?" asked the Tzarevich.

" Because," replied the other, " thou must first pass three rivers. At each river is a ferry, and the price each ferryman asks is a great one, for the first will strike off thy right hand, the second thy left foot, and the third thy head."

" Well," answered Tzarevich Petr, " a man can die but once !" And he thanked him and made to ride on, but the old man stopped him.

" Thou art both brave and courteous too," he said, " and perchance thou mayest cross the three rivers. If thou dost, ride straight on till thou reachest a high mountain, on whose top are the four Palaces of Kastchey. At the base of the mountain is a cave with an iron door. Enter it and thou wilt find four iron claws. Bind these to thy hands and feet and it may be thou wilt be able to reach the top."

The Tzarevich bade the old man and the old woman farewell, rode to the first river and demanded to be ferried over.

"Wilt thou pay me my price?" asked the huge ferryman.

"Time enough to talk of price when thou hast served me thy service," said the Tzarevich, and rode his horse into the boat. So they crossed and when they came to the other side he asked: "What is there to pay?"

"Stretch forth thy right hand," said the ferryman, and drew his sword.

"Nay," answered Tzarevich Petr. "I need my hand myself." And he whipped out his own blade and struck the ferryman such a blow that the steel pierced through the copper armour and killed him. He fell with a crash into the water, and the Tzarevich, pulling the boat high up on the shore, rode on to the second river.

There the like happened. When the gigantic ferryman bade him stretch forth his left foot, the Tzarevich, drawing sword, sprang upon him before his blade had left its scabbard and smote him with a blow that cleaved through the silver plates of his armour and killed him. Then the Tzarevich secured the boat and rode on to the third river. And on its bank stood a wild man, as tall as a giant and as thick as a hay-stack, with a shield, helmet and breast-plate all of gold, and with an oak club in his hand.

Tzarevich Petr, however, was not daunted nor did his horse show fear.   He rode aboard and bade the giant ferry him over, and when they were come to the other side he asked : " What is there to pay ?"

" Stretch out thy neck," said the ferryman, " that I may strike off thy head."

But even as he lifted his huge oak club, the Tzarevich sprang in under his shield and dealt him such a blow with his tested sword that the point shivered the gold breast-plate and killed him. Tzarevich Petr fastened the boat and rode on, and presently he came to a mountain so high that its top was propped against the sky and he could scarce lift his eyes to its summit.   He turned out his good horse to graze on white summer wheat in the open *steppe*, searched till he came upon the iron door and entered the cave.   Here he found the four iron claws, and binding them to his hands and feet, began to climb the mountain.

For a whole month he climbed, higher and higher, and finally he reached the top, which was so high that from it one could see the whole world, with all its countries, spread out as if on the palm of the hand. Here he took off his iron claws, thanked God, and after resting three days, went straight before him.

Whether the way was long or short, he came at length to a vast Palace built all of copper. No guard stood at its gate, and he entered. Each room through which he passed was of copper. In the inmost chamber sat a maiden on a copper chair, embroidering upon a copper frame, and the scissors, the thimble and the needle she used were of copper also. He greeted her and told her his quest.

"This is indeed a Palace of Kastchey, good youth," said the damsel. "I too was stolen away from my father's Tzardom by the Wizard, who comes hither to visit me once every three months. I know naught of thy little mother, but if thou goest further, to Kastchey's second Palace, perchance thou mayest hear of her. The Wizard is hard to conquer, however, and thou art the first who has been able to come thus far. Shouldst thou succeed, I pray thee to remember me and take me back with thee to the white world."

Tzarevich Petr promised her this, and setting out, travelled for the space of a day till he came to a Palace more splendid than the first, built all of silver. It, too, was unguarded, and entering, he found in its further chamber a damsel sitting on a silver stool, weaving on a silver loom with thread of pure silver. Her also he greeted and told his errand.

"I, too," she said, "was stolen away from my father's realm by the Wizard, and brought to this Palace, whither he comes to visit me once every two months. I have not seen thy little mother, but go thou to Kastchey's third Palace, beyond this, and perchance thou mayest hear of her. If thou meetest and art victor over him, forget me not, I beseech thee, but take me with thee to the white world."

The Tzarevich gave the damsel his promise and set out at once, and the next day came to a Palace wealthy and magnificent which blazed like fire in the sunlight, for it was built entirely of gold. Like the others, it was unguarded, so he entered and explored it and in its inmost chamber he found a damsel sitting on a golden divan, making lace upon a golden pillow, and both the shuttle and the thread were of pure gold. The damsel was of such beauty that it could not be described but only told in a tale, and Tzarevich Petr could not look at her enough.

"Health to thee, beautiful maiden!" he said.

"Health to thee, Tzarevich," she replied. "But how comest thou hither? By thine own will or by force?"

"By mine own will," he answered. "I seek my little mother who has been stolen away from my father's Tzardom by Kastchey. Canst thou tell me where she is?"

"Why should I not be able?" she rejoined. "I, too, was stolen from my father's Tzardom by the Wizard, who visits me here once each month. But thy little mother he keeps in his fourth Palace, which is built of pearl, and thither thou must go. But, I implore thee, if thou dost overcome and slay the monster, remember me and take me with thee out into the white world."

"Sooner than leave thee here to Kastchey would I give mine own life!" he answered. "Never fear that I could ever forget thee!"

"Hearken, now," she said. "When thou comest to the last of the Wizard's Palaces, thou wilt see that it lies in a garden which is surrounded like a wall by an enormous serpent coiled with its tail in its mouth. Take this bundle of herbs and when thou comest into the open field about the Palace, choose a spot whence the wind doth blow from thee toward the serpent, and there build a fire and throw some of the herb into the flame. Mind that thou dost not use it all and that thou thyself stand behind the wind. The smoke will cause the serpent to fall asleep and thou mayest then climb over its body and enter the Palace."

Tzarevich Petr bade her farewell and set out, and when he had travelled a day he came to a Palace which rose dazzling white from the midst of a green garden, and all about the garden lay coiled a huge snake, a living, scaly wall. He went into the meadow, built a fire and threw upon it some sprigs of the herbs, and from it arose a great volume of smoke which the wind drove toward the serpent, causing it to fall asleep. He then climbed over it and entered the Palace of pearl.

He passed through room after room till he came to the inmost of all, and there he saw his little mother sitting on a high pearl throne, dressed in a robe of brocade sewn with seed pearls, and wearing a Tzaritza's pearly crown.

When she saw him she ran to him, and em-

bracing him, fell to weeping. "How hast thou
found me here," she cried, "my brave and beloved
son ? For I, thy mother, am in the power of this
mighty Wizard who comes to me each day. Thou
wilt strive to overcome him, yet is he strong in his
enchantments, while thou art but an untried youth,
so that I greatly fear for thee !"

"The wind doth not blow for ever," said the
Tzarevich, and he comforted his mother and they
kissed and caressed one another, when there rose
a roaring of wind so that all the crystal windows
rattled. "Kastchey comes even now," she said.
"Hide thee quickly beneath my mantle !"

He concealed himself and scarce had he done so
when the Wizard entered, green-eyed, naked and
hairy, with a bared sword in his hand and a nose
curved like a scimitar. He hastened to the
Tzaritza and began to pet and fondle her. "Hast
thou been lonely, light of mine eyes ?" he asked.

"Yes," she answered. "Thou travellest far and
hast many enemies and I fear for thy life."

"No fear of that," he said. "My life I carry
not in my body but in another place."

"Where is that place ?" she asked.

"It is in the broom that stands beside the door,"

he answered; "but now I am tired and I would
sleep."

He laid his head on the Tzaritza's knees and
slept, while the Tzarevich lay hidden, and when he
woke he bade her farewell till the morrow and
departed in a whirlwind from the Palace.

Then the Tzaritza went and fetched the broom,
and bringing a quantity of precious stones, bade
Tzarevich Petr sew them all about it. This he did,
when she returned it to its place and they spent
the afternoon in conversation.

Next day, as they sat together, there came again
the sound of the howling wind and a second time
she concealed the Tzarevich beneath her mantle,
when the Wizard entered and began to fondle her
as before. Presently he saw the broom and asked:
"Why, thou dearest of women, hast thou sewn a
common broom with jewels?"

"Because," she replied, "thou didst tell me that
in it was contained thy life and thy life is more
precious to me than many jewels!"

Then he embraced her more tenderly and said
he: "I did but tell thee that to try thee. My life
is not in the broom but is in the hedge that rings
the garden." Then, when he had slept and

refreshed himself, he bade her farewell till the morrow and departed in his whirlwind.

The Tzaritza at once fetched a quantity of gold and said to the Tzarevich: "Go thou and cover the garden hedge with this, every twig and leaf." He did so and they spent the afternoon in conversation as before.

Next day there came again the sound of the shrieking wind, the Tzarevich concealed himself for a third time, and Kastchey entered and began to fondle the Tzaritza. "Love of my heart," he said, "as I came hither I saw that thou hadst covered the garden hedge with gold. Why hast thou done so?"

"For the reason," she answered, "that thou didst tell me thy life was contained within it and thy life is more dear to me than much gold!"

The Wizard caressed her in the most tender fashion. "I did but tell thee that," he said, "to try thee still further. Now, however, I am assured that thou dost truly love me. Know that my life is in neither the broom nor the hedge, but is in an egg. The egg is in a duck, and the duck is in a hare, and the hare nests in a great hollow log that floats in a pond in a forest of the island Bouyan."

KASTCHEY.

Having thus spoken, Kastchey put his head on the Tzaritza's knees and slept, and soon, awaking, bade her farewell and departed.

Then Tzarevich Petr came from his concealment and his mother said: "This time, my dear son, Kastchey has told truly wherein his wicked life lies. Only when thou hast found the egg canst thou overcome him. Go, therefore, with God, for here thy life is in danger each moment."

So he embraced her, and burning in the garden some of the herb which the maiden of the golden Palace had given him, climbed over the serpent and went his way. He passed the gold, the silver, and the copper Palaces without stopping, found his iron claws and began to climb down the mountain. At the end of a month he reached its foot, left the iron claws in the cave, found his horse grazing on the open *steppe*, and set out for the island Bouyan.

He rode a long way and he rode a short way, and at length he came to the sea-ocean. On the sand, gasping out its life, lay a stranded pike-fish, and pitying its plight, the Tzarevich dismounted, picked it up and threw it into the water. Then remounting his good horse, he spurred it into the water and it began to swim to the island Bouyan.

It swam one day, it swam two, and on the third it reached the island, and leaving his steed to rest, Tzarevich Petr went straight to the forest.

He had scarce entered it when he came upon a great bear whose paw was caught beneath a fallen tree. Drawing his sword, he cut the creature loose and went on, and presently he saw an otter fast in a snare. He released the otter, and a little further on he found a hawk struggling in a tangle of vines. He freed the hawk also, and pressing on, soon came to the pond.

In the middle of it floated a great branchless log, but it was beyond his reach. While he wondered what he should do, a heavy rain began to fall and the water of the pond rose. He climbed a tree and when the log floated near he secured it. When the rain ceased and the water fell, he attacked the log with his sword, but so huge was it that he could not cut it though. Suddenly, while he laboured, the bear he had befriended rushed from the wood and tore the log asunder with its great paws. Out of the log leaped a hare, but the otter he had released sprang from the thicket, pursued the hare and caught it and tore it to pieces. From the hare flew a duck, but the hawk he had freed

darted after it into the sky and seized it. The
duck thereupon laid an egg and the egg fell into
the sea, but while the Tzarevich was bemoaning
its loss with tears, there came swimming to the
shore the pike-fish whose life he had saved, bringing the egg in its mouth. Then Tzarevich Petr
put the egg in his belt, mounted his horse, which
swam back with him across the sea-ocean, and
having rested, set out again for the mountain of
Kastchey.

The telling is easy but the labour is hard.
Whether he rode a week or a month, he came at
length to the mountain, left his horse to graze on
the *steppe*, and binding the iron claws to his hands
and feet, climbed to the summit and hastened to
the Palace of pearl. Again he burned some of the
drowsy herb, climbed over the serpent, entered and
embraced his mother and showed her the egg.

Before long there arose the sound of the whistling wind and in came Kastchey. He ground his
teeth when he saw the Tzarevich, and would have
rushed at once upon him, but Tzarevich Petr
squeezed the egg in his hand, ever so slightly, and
as he did so the fierce light grew dim in the
Wizard's eyes. The Tzarevich tossed the egg from

the right hand to the left, and Kastchey was hurled violently from one corner of the room to the other. With a last effort the wicked Wizard strove to reach his enemy with his sword, but Tzarevich Petr threw the egg on the floor. It broke, and instantly Kastchey fell down dead and the serpent that coiled about the garden vanished.

The Tzarevich made a great pyre, burned the body of the Wizard to ashes and scattered the ashes to the winds. Then with his mother he set out on their return. The lovely damsel of the gold Palace met them with joy, and her the Tzarevich kissed on the sugar-sweet mouth and they plighted their troth that moment. Taking her with them, they visited the Palaces of silver and copper, and the maidens imprisoned there welcomed them with gladness and accompanied them.

When they came to the brink of the steep descent, Tzarevich Petr found his iron claws once more, donned them, and tearing into strips the outer robes of the three maidens, twisted a rope by means of which, as he climbed, he lowered them, with his mother, down the mountain. When they reached the level ground, he caught his good steed, set his mother upon it and they and the

three Tzarevnas set out for the Tzardom of his
father.

In the forest which skirted the desert of hot sand,
they came upon the little old man and woman sitting upon two stones.   " So thou hast slain Kastchey !" said the greybeard.   " Now I rejoice also,
for he was my greatest enemy." He gave them
four noble steeds, a milk-white mare to bear the
Tzaritza and stallions of gold, of silver and of
copper colour for the three Tzarevnas, and in this
wise they rode to the Tzardom of Tzar Bel-Belianin.

When they drew near to the capital, the Tzarevich sent in advance a swift messenger to the Tzar
with this message: " Little father! I, thy son
Petr, am returning home, bringing with me my
mother the Tzaritza, my own bride to be, who is a
maiden as lovely as the stars, and Tzarevnas for my
two brothers.   Come thou out to meet us."

The Tzar, hearing the message, could not believe
his ears.   He mounted and rode out of the capital
at the head of all his Ministers and Boyars and his
army, and when he saw that it was indeed true and
that his well-loved Tzaritza was alive, his joy knew
no bounds.   He ordered the musicians to play their
instruments and the drummers to beat their drums,

and bringing them to the Palace decreed a great festival whose splendour made the whole Tzardom wonder.

When the feastings were ended, Tzarevich Petr wedded the lovely damsel of the golden Palace, and the maidens of the silver and copper Palaces were wed to his brothers the Tzareviches Alexé and Dimitry. And soon after Tzar Bel-Belianin laid down his sceptre and Tzarevich Petr ruled the Tzardom after him. He rejoiced in his good fortune without boasting, his subjects loved and feared him, and his life was long and his reign glorious.

THE END.